LONG ISLAND
A NATURAL HISTORY

LONG ISLAND

A NATURAL HISTORY

TEXT AND PHOTOGRAPHS BY
ROBERT VILLANI

HARRY N. ABRAMS, INC., PUBLISHERS

For my wife Miriam and my daughters Sophie and Juliet

Editor: Eric Himmel
Designer: Ellen Nygaard Ford

Library of Congress Cataloging-in-Publication Data

Villani, Robert.
Long Island : a natural history / text and photographs by
Robert Villani.
          p.   cm.
   Includes bibliographical references and index.
   ISBN 0-8109-3591-0 (cloth)
   1. Natural history–New York (State)–Long Island.   I. Title.
QH105.N7V55   1997
508.747'21–dc21   97-7632

Printed and bound in Japan

 Harry N. Abrams, Inc.
100 Fifth Avenue
New York, N.Y. 10011
www.abramsbooks.com

INTRODUCTION

Natural history, the attempt to describe the plants and animals that live in a particular place, is first and foremost a science of observation. This book, about the natural history of Long Island, is the result of observations made and recorded with a camera over a decade of intensive exploration of the landscape in which I grew up and formed my first impressions of the world. As any nature photographer will attest, each separate observation can absorb hundreds of hours of searching, stalking, and patient waiting. To write this book, I have also called upon the published observations of hundreds of other naturalists and scientists.

Observation alone, however, can only build up a picture of a scene; to understand how a natural scene came about and what sustains it, we must turn to the earth sciences and the life sciences. In the case of Long Island, an intricate and highly variegated natural scene becomes immediately more comprehensible in the light of geology.

The earth is changing all the time, but unless we live in areas that are threatened by such cataclysms as earthquakes and volcanoes, the dynamic processes that shape our natural environment seem remote and abstract. Our everyday sense of time is inevitably shaped by the average human life span of seventy to eighty years; the earth is 4.6 billion years old, and we typically measure geological events in its history in the tens or hundreds of thousands of years. Some parts of the earth's surface do, however, change at a rate that is meaningful in the context of human consciousness and history, and Long Island is such a place.

Long Island as we know it did not exist when human civilization began and has altered appreciably in the span of memory. Although its rudimentary beginnings predate the age of dinosaurs, its present form is hardly more than six to eight thousand years old—an artifact of the last ice age. As readers of the first chapter of this book will discover, Long Island consists mainly of millions and millions of tons of soil, sand, clay, and rocks deposited by glaciers that advanced slowly southward across New England. The glaciers melted as the climate grew warmer, and the seas rose around the land.

Imagine trying to decipher a page upon which the writing had been crudely erased and overprinted with new words many times over; the record left by glaciers upon Long Island's surface was no less complex. The glaciers deposited fertile soils in some areas and sterile sands in others, determining what types of plant and animal communities would subsequently colonize the newborn land. Its rich western and northern regions would became vastly diverse in plant life, containing over eighty-eight native species of trees alone, while the great sandy plains of its interior would be dominated by pitch pines and heaths, except for one curious region of prairie, known as the Hempstead Plains.

Following the glaciers' retreat, the omnipresent forces of erosion—wind and water—replaced glaciers as the primary shapers of Long Island's countenance, albeit on a much less dramatic scale. Wave action has both added to and taken away from the work of the glaciers. The Atlantic Ocean has piled sand into long thin ribbons along the island's South Shore, forming barrier islands with their shallow bays and marshes that are so productive of life. But the ocean is also relentlessly eroding the glacial deposits of the Montauk peninsula. These changes can be observed from year to year and sometimes—as during and after a hurricane—from day to day.

The chapters of this book neatly divide the natural communities of Long Island into groups that can be clearly explained by the geological history of the land and the dynamic forces of the sea.

Geography is also a significant variable in natural history. Long Island's location along the Eastern Seaboard has been an important factor in the evolution of its flora and fauna. The island lies on the North American coastal plain, poised between the Canadian zone to the north and the Carolinian zone to the south. Here the two life zones blend and merge into a mosaic of southern and northern species of life. Additionally, the Atlantic flyway, a major migratory route for North American birds, crosses over Long Island. More than 180 species of birds have bred on Long Island and many more migrants occur regularly.

Curiously, migrating species appear to find Long Island more hospitable than do neighboring species, and the island's relationship with the mainland that it hugs so closely is a puzzle to naturalists. Many animals and plants that would seem well equipped to make the journey have not done so. Mainland species such as the barred owl, pileated woodpecker, wood turtle, fence lizard, and five-lined skink are representative of a much longer list of organisms that are capable of colonizing Long Island, but for some mysterious reason never have.

No less important than geology and geography in determining the course of natural history is the degree of human intervention in the landscape, which, in the case of Long Island, suddenly reduces the majestic timescale of nature's changes into the narrow space of a few lifetimes. Unfortunately the beauty and integrity of Long Island's natural communities have been under steady assault since the arrival of European settlers in the early seventeenth century. Long Island's proximity to New York City resulted in a constant drain of its impressive resources and an ever increasing population pressure on the land. The island supplied the city with cordwood, lumber for building, farmland, and the sea's resources, diminishing forever its pristine nature. Early on, the forests were cut, and today little of the original primary growth remains. Before the European settlement, Long Island had also been rich in water—fresh water that flowed throughout the interior as springs, streams, and rivers fed by enormous underground reservoirs called aquifers, relics of the ice age. The felling of forests and human demands for water quickly lowered the water table, and most of the island's numerous springs and brooks vanished, never to return.

The years following World War II saw drastic changes in the wake of unprecedented suburban sprawl. The once vast Hempstead Plains were reduced to a remnant in a matter of ten years. Now orderly rows of thousands of houses cover ground once blanketed by wildflowers. From Long Island's western tip in Brooklyn, through Queens and most of Nassau County, the island is a meshwork of roads and buildings with little open space. Only in Suffolk County do we find any appreciably large undeveloped areas.

If they have shrunk, the natural communities on Long Island have also endured. Through the years there has emerged a growing group of Long Islanders that recognizes the ecological importance and beauty of our land, and much has been done to preserve what remains of Long Island's natural heritage. Hopefully others will join in this effort. Only through education and action will nature's Long Island abide.

CHAPTER 1

GEOLOGY

The east coast of the United States is characterized by a broad, gently sloping coastal plain that extends from the foothills of the Appalachian mountains to the Atlantic Ocean. Along much of the coast, barrier islands a short distance offshore nestle shallow bays and protect the mainland from the fury of the sea. The curious shape of Long Island abruptly alters this pattern where the mid-Atlantic and the New England states meet. It is as if a great piece of the coastal plain, complete with barrier islands and shallow bays, had broken away from the mainland.

The native Americans who first settled on Long Island called the land Paumanok, meaning fish-shaped. From the air Long Island indeed resembles a large lumbering fish taking shelter at the mouth of New York Harbor and splashing its tail in the turbulent waters of the Atlantic. At the island's eastern end, the North and South forks outline the fish's tailfins; at the western end, Jamaica Bay is its mouth. Lloyd Neck to the north and the barrier islands along the South Shore form the fish's dorsal and ventral fins; the long ridge of high ground that extends along the length of the island's North Shore its backbone.

According to geological time, this fish has only recently arrived on the scene, six to eight thousand years ago. Given the 4.56 billion years age of the earth, it is easy to see why Long Island is considered a geological infant. Despite its superficial youth, however, the island's rudimentary beginnings can be traced back 250 million years, to an era predating the age of dinosaurs. The gentle landscape of Long Island is the result of a progression of dynamic earth processes spanning this time.

To understand fully the forces that formed Long Island, we must acquaint ourselves with a few geological concepts. First is the impermanence of rock. In human terms, rock is an enduring material, which is why we turn to it in construction when durability is needed. But from the perspective of geological time, the instability of rock is apparent. Deep underground, pressure and heat transform rock into magma, a molten mass that flows like thick molasses beneath the earth's crust. Meanwhile, rock exposed on the earth's surface is subject to the irre-

sistible forces of erosion: given a sufficient amount of time, wind and water will reduce even the most rugged mountains to rolling plains. Furthermore, eroded material carried to the sea by rivers may consolidate and form new sedimentary rock formations.

Another important geological concept is the transient nature of landforms. Beginning in the 1960s, geologists developed a theory of plate tectonics that ties together geological science much as the theory of evolution resolved disparate problems in biology. They recognized that the lithosphere—the hard outer layer of the earth composed of the crust and the upper mantle—is formed of rigid, continent-sized plates separated by tectonic boundaries. The present configuration of the earth's landmasses is now understood to be an ever-changing mosaic of continental and oceanic plates. These plates are always moving, albeit at a yearly rate that is virtually imperceptible, creating astounding changes over millions of years.

Radioactive isotopes—latent primordial heat from the earth's early history—and a small amount of heat released by the continuing crystallization of the earth's molten metal outer core account for the energy that fuels the processes of plate tectonics. These sources of heat manifest themselves as convection cells of molten rock—magma—that slowly move in currents within the earth's mantle. The magma releases itself as lava at the midoceanic ridges found along many tectonic boundaries below the seas. At these tectonic boundaries the cooling magma forms rock, and this new material forces the plates further apart where it accumulates, resulting in the drift of continents. At tectonic boundaries called subduc-

tion zones, oceanic and continental crust forces its way back into the earth's mantle, impelled by the constant force of the midoceanic ridge spreading, thus completing the circle of crust formation and destruction. When the consumed crust reaches a critical depth, it becomes molten lava again. The Pacific coast of the United States offers a clear example of the tectonic cycle at work. A short distance offshore, subduction is forcing an oceanic plate under the west coast of the United States. The resulting magma rises to the surface, forming a long volcanic chain running from Washington to California. The 1980 eruption of Mount St. Helens was a reminder of the potency of tectonic processes.

Although Long Island does not seem to have been the site of cataclysmic geological events, a close examination of the geologic record—recorded in layers of sand, clay, gravel, and silt—reveals a complex history of tectonic forces.

More than 240 million years ago, during the Paleozoic era, great shallow seas covered much of what is now North America, and the arrangement of the earth's continental plates was quite different from what we know today. At the end of the Paleozoic, the continental plates apparently collided and fused into one landmass, the so-called supercontinent, Pangaea. The eastern edge of the North American plate came together with a portion of the western bulge of the African plate.

The creation of Pangaea lowered the seafloor and caused the formation of great mountain ranges, among them the Appalachians, as the plates collided and buckled. Towering more than three miles high, the ancient Appalachians were one of the greatest mountain ranges ever to appear on Earth. The material that was to become the bedrock of Long Island lay in the eastern foothills of these massive peaks. Eventually, about two hundred million years ago, tectonic forces broke up Pangaea, and the continents began to drift toward their present positions, leaving the Appalachians on the eastern coast of North America.

The following Mesozoic era saw the erosion, by wind and water, of this mighty mountain range into a series of rolling hills known as a peneplain. The rivers that flowed from the Appalachians carried vast quantities of debris eastward to the Atlantic, depositing it there as sediment on the ocean floor. By the middle of the Mesozoic era, during the Jurassic period, the earth's crust was again subject to massive disturbances. On the west coast of North America the Pacific and North American plates collided, forcing an upheaval of material that formed the Rocky Mountains. The resulting shock waves of this orogeny—or mountain-building episode—had significant effects on the east coast, where the land tilted until its eastern-most confines lay under the waters of the Atlantic Ocean. The bedrock that is the foundation of Long Island was now in place in shallow seas a short distance from shore.

During the Cretaceous period at the end of the Mesozoic, some one hundred million years ago, the next phase in the development of Long Island began. The tilting of the peneplain caused the rejuvenation of streams and rivers, ushering in a new period of erosion. Eroded material transported by rivers formed deltas, mud flats, and sandbars in the shallow seas. Over approximately forty million years a vast quantity of sedimentary material, mostly sand and clay, formed

a layer on top of the submerged bedrock in the Long Island area.

The bedrock foundation of Long Island is known as Fordham Gneiss. It is a metamorphosed sedimentary stone formed by the great pressure and heat generated by tectonic activity. The Cretaceous sediments and the stratas that followed completely cover the bedrock, except for a small portion of exposed rock in western Long Island in Astoria, Queens. The basement rock is close to the surface in western Long Island but from there it dips in a southeasterly direction at a rate of eighty feet per mile. At Brookhaven National Laboratory near Riverhead a deep well intersected the bedrock at fifteen hundred feet below the surface.

The Mesozoic era ended sixty-five million years ago, giving way to the Cenozoic era. Shortly thereafter the relentless persistence of the earth's geological forces initiated another period of change for the Long Island region. The tilting of the peneplain became more pronounced. As the land thrust upward at its western edge, the ancient seas receded, forming a new shoreline and coastal plain from the soft, unconsolidated Cretaceous strata that had been on the ocean's bottom. This sedimentary layer was relatively thin where it met the newly re-formed Appalachians to the west. Its thickness increased as the plain extended in an easterly direction toward what we might call the Long Island region, even though it was now simply a part of the larger landmass and not an island. The raising of the land above sea level terminated the deposition of sediments on Long Island for the time being and initiated a new period of erosion.

From the Long Island region the coastline continued in a northeasterly direction to what is now Connecticut. Rivers and streams on the Connecticut plateau turbulently coursed their way toward what was to be Long Island. The intense erosive action of these rivers produced a deep trough running in an east to west direction through the soft Cretaceous sediments just north of the Long Island region. In time the trough widened, forming a broad shallow valley where Long Island Sound is today. The river courses are not entirely clear from the geological record. In all likelihood, the Connecticut River and its numerous tributaries stripped the land of its Cretaceous sediments in their easterly race to the sea, which accounts for the depth of many of the harbors on Long Island's North Shore. One tributary of the Connecticut River that flowed in a westerly direction cut a valley that later became the East River on Long Island's western border.

The changes that shaped Long Island as we know it today began roughly one million years ago, during the Pleistocene epoch of the Cenozoic era, virtually on the doorstep of our own time. With the advent of the Cenozoic era, the worldwide warm and mild climate characteristic of the Mesozoic era had gradually cooled. During the Pleistocene epoch, the mean world temperature dropped drastically enough to allow for the existence of permanent ice. Thus began the invasion of Long Island by glaciers.

Glaciers are large masses of ice capable of movement across land. They form when the yearly accumulation of snow in a region exceeds the yearly rate of melting. Eventually, so much snow accumulates that its own weight compresses it into ice. Where the glacial ice meets the bedrock, the weight of

Rocky shoreline at Montauk Point State Park.

the mass above creates enough heat from friction to cause melting. As water flows out and refreezes, the glacier slides along the slick wet surface, pulled by gravity. It is by this process that glaciers advance, like huge snakes slinking along the contours of the landscape. Presently, in the cold regions of the earth, such as Greenland, Alaska, and Antarctica, large glaciers endure. Smaller glaciers can be found at the tops of many of the world's higher mountain ranges, subsisting in the cool climatic conditions provided by great elevation.

Geologists do not fully understand the processes that initiate continental glaciation. During times of plate congregation, the resulting increased landmass appears to sequester carbon dioxide, hindering the greenhouse effect and thus lowering the mean world temperature. The intense volcanic activity often associated with plate movement also may lower mean world temperature by injecting large amounts of particulate matter into the upper atmosphere, where it ultimately blocks the sun's warming rays. For obvious reasons, glaciation is also likely when the plate tectonic process nudges continents closer to the earth's poles. An astronomical phenomenon known as the Milankovitch Cycles seems to influence glaciation once the process begins. These regular but minor changes in the earth's orbit appear to be responsible for the small glacial retreats and advances that shaped the superficial landforms of Long Island.

It is hard to imagine ice as an agent of devastation and change, yet when in the form of an advancing glacier, ice becomes an invincible force capable of radically reshaping the engulfed landscape.

To begin with, a glacier may fracture the underlying bedrock. Meltwater at the base of the glacier seeps into the crevices and cleavage lines found in most rock outcrops and refreezes. The expansion of the freezing water breaks off pieces of bedrock. The loose fragments, called till, are swept up by the flowing ice, exposing a virgin layer of rock to the seeping water. Through this seemingly innocuous process, a glacier can carve great cavities in the sides of mountains or literally shear the top off an entire mountain range.

The till, ranging in size from particles as fine as baby powder to boulders as large as a house, may be transported hundreds of miles by a glacier before a warming climate checks its advance. Like stones caught in a farmer's plow, the till scrapes and reshapes the surface, giving birth to a new landscape. At times the ice-borne grit polishes rock surfaces to a smooth, mirrorlike luster, or the suspended till etches small scratch marks into rock outcrops, recording the direction of the glacier's movement.

A number of land modifications occur when glaciers retreat as well. A glacier ceases to advance when it melts faster than new ice can accumulate. Massive amounts of water released by melting glaciers carry with them and subsequently deposit the suspended till, which is then called drift, accumulated during their journey. Along with modeling Long Island's surface and defining its present form, the glacial deposits of the last ice age have served as a blueprint for the vegetation and ecosystems presently flourishing.

Flowing southward along the curvature of the earth, the southern edge of the continental ice sheet made at least two advances to the Long Island area in the

Pleistocene epoch. The glaciers' advance was slow, perhaps no more than one hundred feet each year, but their stamp was enduring. In the wake of their retreat, the familiar form of Long Island appeared.

The first ice advance to the Long Island region occurred during what is called the Mannetto-Jameco stage of Long Island's geological evolution. Subsequent invasions of ice obliterated most of the traces of this advance; however, it is known that an outwash plain, the Mannetto Plain, approximately three hundred feet high, gradually accumulated on top of the Cretaceous strata. An outwash plain is the delta of sediment that is laid down at the end of a fluvial flow, such as a glacier, stream, or river. A warming climate initiated the retreat of this maiden ice sheet, exposing the plain to the ravages of erosion, and within a relatively short time it was reduced to only a few isolated knolls. These features persist today as Wheatley Hills, Mannetto Hills or West Hills, and Half Hollow Hills in the area of the Nassau/Suffolk county line. Cretaceous sediments define the hills' heights more so than the thin Mannetto deposits that cap them.

The Gardiners interglacial stage followed the Mannetto-Jameco ice retreat. During this interglacial period silty clays carried by streams from the New England region accumulated on Long Island. The climate at this time was similar to that of the present-day Maine coast. This short period of subsistence was followed by another glacial advance.

The following Manhasset stage again saw the Long Island region entombed in ice. This second glacier was more powerful than the first. As the ice approached the

A glacial erratic lies wedged in the cliffs at Target Rock National Wildlife Refuge in Lloyd Neck.

Overleaf:
The spectacular "hoodoo" formations along the Atlantic shore bluffs at Montauk Point State Park are caused by the differential erosion by wind and water of sand and more resistant bands of clay.

southern New England region, it forced very fine sand from the Connecticut valley southward toward Long Island. The arrival of this transitional sediment signaled the end of the Gardiners interglacial stage and its incidence on Long Island marks the boundary between the Manhasset advances and those that occurred earlier.

The Manhasset stage was characterized by three major glacial advances. During the Herod advance, the continental glacier formed an ice front more than one thousand feet in height that came to rest for a time in the valley that later became Long Island Sound. The meltwater streams that ran off of this stalled glacial terminus carried with them fine clays, sands, and gravels, forming huge deltas of sediment. These depositions gave height to northern Long Island, forming most of today's North Shore bluffs.

The subsequent Montauk advance extended further south than the Herod, eventually engulfing and causing minor changes in the Herodian depositions. When a glacier's rate of melting at its terminus equals the rate of its forward movement, the glacier's end is stationary, but the ice within the glacier continues to advance and move material forward. The result is an accumulation of debris at the stalled end, creating a pile of rubble known as a moraine. The Ronkonkoma Moraine—a coarse pile of till in the middle of Long Island—extends from Nassau County and along the South Fork to Montauk Point. The meltwater flowing in alluvial patterns deposited a layer of sand and gravel in a great outwash plain south of the Ronkonkoma highlands.

Later, the glacier retreated slightly and again stalled. Similar to the Ronkonkoma Moraine and north of it, the resulting Harbor Hill Moraine, the "backbone" of our fish-shaped island, runs from Brooklyn east along the North Fork to Orient Point. An outwash plain also developed south of the Harbor Hill Moraine, but it was smaller and of less coarse material than the plain south of the Ronkonkoma Moraine.

The final ice advance, the Wisconsin advance, was of a short duration yet its impact was significant. The Wisconsin ice overrode the various formations created by the previous advances, rounding hills, smoothing the land, and depositing a layer of permeable brown till over the region's surface. The till layer, only about four feet thick, acts like a sponge, absorbing rainwater that seeps into lower water-bearing sands where it forms aquifers that are the source of Long Island's fresh water.

It was only about eleven thousand years ago that a warming climate finally began to melt the great mantle of ice that covered so much of the Northern Hemisphere. We are still enjoying this warm interglacial stage, but the scientific consensus is that in the not too distant geological future another cooling trend, complete with accompanying continental glaciation, will commence. Approximately four thousand years ago the seas rose to today's level, flooding the valley north of the glacial hills and outwash plains, which is now called Long Island Sound, and the land between the two moraines to the east, producing Peconic Harbor.

The Pleistocene glaciation left behind a Long Island that would be recognizable today. The sea was next to make its mark on the island, as thousands of years of wind and water sculpted the coast. Wave action on the South Shore gouged beaches, depositing their sand and gravel a short distance offshore and forming barrier islands and protected lagoons. On the North Shore, the effects have been less severe. Intense wave action in eastern Long Island Sound chiseled the once-jagged shores into the smooth coastline of today, but to the west, where the waves of the sound are less harsh, the land retains its rugged profile.

Today, with the exception of its barrier islands, Long Island's landmass seems to have stabilized. Geologists, however, have observed that change on earth occurs at regular intervals. In the geological record we find evidence of long periods of uniformity abruptly altered by catastrophic geological events. Humanity has enjoyed a period of relative calm, but at some point drastic changes will occur. If civilization survives its current self-inflicted problems, sometime in the future it might face its ultimate challenge: coping with the ramifications of major geological change.

Long Island's dry outwash plains are the perfect habitat for butterfly weed (*Ascelpias tuberosa*), seen here in a small clearing in Connetquot State Park.

Overleaf:
Glaciation left numerous kettle hole depressions all across Long Island, like this vernal pond in Brookville.

CHAPTER 2

BARRIER ISLANDS

Like many large islands, Long Island itself harbors numerous smaller islands of various sizes, shapes, and origins. Barrier islands, in particular, have a significant role in preserving Long Island's varied habitats. A short distance from Long Island's South Shore, delicate ribbons of white sand stretch for miles, cradling the mainland and providing pristine beaches to the delight of countless individuals who sunbathe, swim, and fish on their shores. Few of them are aware of these islands' primary importance in shielding the mainland of Long Island from the fury of the Atlantic. Were these islands to disappear, wave action would quickly begin to eat away the unconsolidated gravels and sands of Long Island's South Shore.

The barrier islands also shelter a number of distinct plant and animal communities, adding to the biological diversity of Long Island. The large shallow lagoons, rich in beauty and varied in life, that have formed between the barrier islands and the mainland are probably the most significant of these habitats, but the islands themselves are home to flora and fauna not found elsewhere.

The barrier islands extend the length of Long Island's South Shore from Rockaway Inlet, Queens, in the west, to the South Fork in the east, and include Rockaway Beach, Long Beach, Jones Beach, Fire Island National Seashore, and the Hampton beaches. They are one of the most recent additions to the Long Island landscape, first making their appearance shortly after the glacial retreat and are probably no more than eight to ten thousand years old. The birth of Long Island's barrier islands began with the formation of a submerged sandbar a short distance offshore caused by the breaking action of waves over the sandy shallows that extend out for miles from the beach. It seems that under the proper conditions, the slightest variation in the height of the ocean floor is sufficient to cause this process to begin, and eventually the constant wave action deposits enough material to elevate the sand bar above the surface, creating a long island of sand roughly parallel to the mainland. Barrier islands are among nature's most malleable landforms due to their close association with the sea. Waves wash up on Long Island's barrier beaches at a slight angle, known as the angle of incidence, only to flow back to the sea at an equivalent but opposite angle, known as the angle of reflection. Where the incoming waves meet the receding waves a longshore current forms, flowing parallel to the beach, often behind a submerged sandbar. Along the barrier beaches of Long Island's South Shore this current runs in a predominately east to west direction. The ceaseless waves pick up sand from the beach and carry it out to sea, where it then gets caught in the longshore drift until it is returned to the beach at a point further west. Over the last 250 years, nearly six miles of land have been added to the western end of Fire Island as the longshore current has carried sand there from as far east as Montauk Point.

The fierce winter storms and occasional hurricanes that assault Long Island pose an acute challenge to the stability of the barrier islands. High winds and violent waves open new inlets by breaching the dunes and opening a path for seawater to flow across the land into the lagoons beyond. On occasion, entire sections of the islands have been returned to the sea.

While longshore currents and storms account for the most significant changes to the barrier islands' topography, other factors account for the existence of sand dunes, which are the most obvious feature of the seashore landscape. The relatively gentle wave action of summer creates small berms and runnels of sand running parallel to the shore on the lower portions of beaches. These small ridges are washed away with the summer beach each winter, but often on a flat sandy area beyond a berm an irregularity, such as a pile of shells or a piece of driftwood, acts as an obstruction to onshore winds, causing them to drop sand on the leeward side of the obstacle. Quickly the small ridge of sand increases in height and length, growing within the wind shadow of the obstruction. As the dunes become more prominent, they invite the specialized plants that are able to flourish in the protection they offer from direct exposure to the sea.

American beach grass (*Ammophila breviligulata*) thrives in this inhospitable environment and is the first plant to colonize the sterile sand ridges. The tickling of windblown sands on the beach grass's emergent stems stimulates the grass's growth so that it is actually more vigorous where sand is being deposited. The plant's extensive rhizomes (underground stems) and deep fibrous roots reach out like grasping hands and act as anchors, not only for the grass but more critically for the sand as well. Eventually the ridges colonized by the beach grass capture enough sand and other material to form a long dune lateral to the ocean.

While the continued growth of beach grass further anchors this dune, another dune between it and the sea may develop in the same manner: the dune system closest to the ocean is called the primary dune and any dunes behind the primary dune are called secondary dune systems. The swale (hollow) between the primary and secondary dunes becomes a specialized environment for a variety of plants and animals. Most of Long Island's barrier beaches display this primary/secondary dune pattern, although at any one time, portions of the beach may have lost their dunes entirely in winter storms.

Occasionally, when the onshore winds are high, the dunes resemble volcanoes as clouds of sand rise from their tops to fill the air and eventually be deposited on the dune's leeward side. A barrier island migrates toward the main-

Gulls roosting on the
barrier island beach at
Moriches Inlet.

Opposite:
The broad, sandy beach
at Jones Beach State
Park in winter.

A common spider crab
(Libinia emarginata) washed up on the shore of the Great South Bay on Fire Island National Seashore.

Two herring gull *(Larus argentatus)* chicks less than a week old sit huddled on a beach at Captree Island awaiting the return of their parents. The chicks' downy covering is cryptically marked like that of the sand, imparting an effective camouflage from predators. Herring gulls are colonial nesting birds whose nests are usually shallow depressions lined with straw, either in the open sand of the beach or hidden among dune grasses.

land as wind-borne sand is carried beyond the secondary dunes, while the ocean's bite reduces the primary dune. The protected hollows that develop behind the dunes often remain stable for long periods of time. It is in this area, in the shadow of the secondary dune, that a sunken forest may develop. The Sunken Forest on Fire Island is the finest example of this special habitat on Long Island.

If you could slice a barrier island in half and examine the face of the cut from the ocean to the bay, an interesting pattern of varied habitats is evident. The sandy beach from the foot of the primary dune to where the continental shelf drops off to deep water is the first such habitat, comprising three interdependent zones of life.

The sublittoral zone begins at the low tide line and extends out into the Atlantic to the edge of the continental shelf. An abundance of swimming organisms occupies this region, including finfish, jellyfish, and occasionally sea mammals, but most characteristic of the sublittoral off Long Island's barrier beaches is the abundance of bottom dwellers. Anyone who has walked the shoreline at Fire Island or Jones Beach has surely seen the large shells of the Atlantic surf clam *(Spisula solidissima)*. They are the largest bivalves that live in Long Island's waters and favor sandy bottoms, where they thrive in the strong wave action and tidal currents of the barrier beach. They anchor themselves by burrowing into the sand and feed on microscopic plants and animals that they filter out of seawater. During severe storms—particularly in the winter—they often will be uprooted and washed ashore, where their shells litter the beach, resembling crude ashtrays, a destiny many of them fulfill when collected and brought home by beachcombers.

The littoral zone—or intertidal zone—includes the area from the high tide's wrack line to the low tide mark. This narrow strip, occupying no more than the ambiguous border between water and land, harbors an abundance of life: it is a dynamic region where plants and animals have evolved to endure the fury of breaking waves and the endless fluctuations of the tides. Although as often dry as it is submerged, few terrestrial species have exploited the intertidal zone, leaving marine flora and fauna full reign of its varied niches.

These plants and animals have evolved to endure the effects of tidal withdrawal, including extreme temperature fluctuation and the desiccating effects of the blazing sun and stiff winds. When the tide is low, the barrier beach reveals an apron of white compressed sand sloping gently toward the sea. Countless small crustaceans make their home in this seemingly lifeless environment. Sand amphipods *(Haustorius arenarius)* are gilled air breathers about half an inch long that are protected by rigid plates along the sides of their flattened bodies. Their three pairs of hind legs are for jumping, while the three front pairs serve as flippers for swimming, the combination making them superbly adapted for intertidal life. They feed on nutrients extracted from water, which they draw in through special feeding appendages, and they are able to perform this task underground using the water trapped between grains of sand.

As a breaking wave rushes back to the sea, close observation will reveal thousands of tiny feathery objects rising from the sand and waving at the receding tide as if in celebration of the arrival of the nourishing water. These are really little mouths, the feeding appendages of the Atlantic mole crab (*Emerita talpoida*), or sand crab, another small crustacean common along the barrier beaches. The largest females are about the size and shape of a human thumb from the tip to the first joint. Their streamlined shape and special appendages for excavating and anchoring make them efficient diggers, able to burrow themselves below the sand in a matter of seconds. At times large numbers of mole crabs rise from the sand at once and scurry up or down the beach slope to a more favorable feeding location. These and other small invertebrates serve as the base of a large food chain dependent on the intertidal zone.

Gulls and other water birds are common around the intertidal zone. Herring gulls (*Larus argentatus*), ring-billed gulls (*Larus delawarensis*), and greater black-backed gulls (*Larus marinus*) are ever-present and, when not pilfering snacks from swimmers and sunbathers, usually dine on crabs, clams, and other seashore offerings.

During the winter Long Island's barrier beaches host the sanderling (*Calidris alba*), a small sandpiper as pale as the sand itself that breeds in the high Arctic and winters along the east coast of the United States. Sanderlings patrol the shores for food in merry little flocks. In unison, they rush away from incoming waves then abruptly charge the ebbing surf searching for tiny crustaceans and worms hidden in the wet sand. Other wintering shorebirds on the barrier islands include dunlins (*Calidris alpina*), ruddy turnstones (*Arenaria interpres*), greater yellowlegs (*Tringa melanoleuca*), black-bellied plovers (*Pluvialis squatarola*), and, favoring the rock jetties and groins, purple sandpipers (*Calidris maritima*).

Beach grass (*Ammophila breviligulata*) thrives along the tops of sandy dunes where other plants would surely perish.

Overleaf:
A view down the swale between the primary dune and the secondary dune systems that protects the Sunken Forest on Fire Island National Seashore.

Common terns (*Sterna hirundo*) are nesting seabirds that have large colonies at several locations on Long Island's barrier beaches.

American oystercatchers (*Haematopus palliatus*) can often be found on the mud flats of the Jamaica Bay Wildlife Refuge. Fifteen years ago they were virtually absent from Long Island, but since then they have expanded their range from the south, and today groups of more than eighty individuals have been observed there.

The third zone is the upper beach, or supralittoral, that extends from the intertidal wrack line to the base of the primary dune. This is the most inhospitable and sparsely populated of the three littoral zones. Unlike the primary dune, whose beach grass-anchored sand is relatively stable, the shifting sands of the dry, windy, often wave-washed upper beach cannot support vegetative growth. Its predominately quartz sands are blinding white on a bright sunny day and, were it not for the summer heat, might pass for snow. Occasionally, the charming purple hue of garnet grains spreads across the white sands in what looks like rippled stains of spilt wine. The sea and wind's propensity for separating the beach's constituents by their specific gravity and mass accounts for these bands.

The wrack line, which marks the border of the intertidal region, is the most important part of the upper beach. Among the wrack—consisting of material left behind by the high tide—is found a collection of seaside organisms, both dead and alive, making it an accurate indicator of littoral and sublittoral inhabitants and their health. The bulk of the wrack is usually made up of seaweed that provides moisture and shelter to a variety of creatures who thrive in this unlikely habitat. Beach fleas (*Talorchestia spp.*), a small amphipod of the upper beach, find the wrack especially inviting, as do flies and midges that lay their eggs in the decaying flesh of marine creatures. Crows, gulls, and shorebirds are frequent visitors scouring the wrack for these hidden treasures.

The rest of the upper beach supports little life, although there are several species of water birds that nest here. Some species are colonial nesters—colonial birds nest in large groups—while others are relatively solitary. The American oystercatcher (*Haematopus palliatus*) is, in both appearance and its distinctive piercing cry, a stunning member of this group. A southern species that has recently expanded its range northward, the large, noisy flocks of the once rare oystercatcher are now a common sight on Long Island. The birds prefer to lay their big, speckled, sand-colored eggs in a small hollow on the white sand of the upper beach.

The least tern (*Sterna antillarum*), an endangered species and our smallest tern, possesses nesting requirements that restrict it to the unblemished sand of the upper beach. Like the oystercatcher, it lays its cryptically decorated eggs in nothing more than a slight depression, relying on the eggs' apparent invisibility to protect them from predators. The terns nest in large groups that tend to keep such predators as raccoons and foxes at bay. When one approaches, the birds will swarm the skies above the intruder, uttering piercing cries and sometimes diving and striking the invader with pinpoint accuracy. Common terns (*Sterna hirundo*), which are certainly the most common tern on Long Island, nest on the upper beach in large colonies but also use other coastal zones for nesting. Occasionally the endangered roseate tern (*Sterna dougallii*), an especially elegant bird that is maritime in habit, usually coming to shore only to breed, can be found nesting among the common terns. On Long Island the various species of terns feed on a variety of small fish that they catch in the ocean, bays, and estuaries, and their survival is dependent on the health and productivity of these waters.

The black skimmer (*Rynchops niger*) is a large ternlike bird with a peculiar call—it sounds like a barking dog—and an even more peculiar bill. The lower mandible is longer than the upper, giving the bill a deformed, useless appearance, yet this clumsy appendage is marvelously adapted to its unique style of fishing. The bird flies gracefully just over the water's surface, "skimming" the water with its protruding lower mandible. When a small fish strikes it, the two mandibles crash together instantly, locking the prey in a viselike grip. It is without doubt one of the most memorable sights you may come across while strolling the barrier beaches.

The bird most often associated with the barrier beach is the piping plover (*Charadrius melodus*). It too is a nationally endangered species, disappearing with the undisturbed white sand beaches it requires to breed. On Long Island we find the piping plovers' highest known breeding concentrations. It is thoroughly a creature of the beaches: so superbly camouflaged that it often goes unnoticed until uttering its plaintive, bell-like piping call. These birds nest on the sand and then feed and shelter their young at various stations along the beach from shore to wrack line to dune and swale.

The primary dune is next in our island cross section. Primary dunes separate the beach from the rest of the barrier island and often resemble long winding walls adorned with a shining mane of beach grass, sturdily shielding the interior from the surf and wind. On the seaward side of the dune few plants besides the beach grass are able to survive in the difficult growing conditions of salt wind, high surface temperatures, and sand accumulation. A few plants have adapted to this environment by developing thick, succulent

leaves to conserve water. In summer the violet blossoms of beach pea (*Lathyrus japonicus*) lie hidden among the dune grass. Beach pea is an edible species of the legume family that closely resembles cultivated peas and was once a source of food for Native Americans and colonists. In early autumn the brilliant flower heads of seaside goldenrod (*Solidago sempervirens*) splash the silvery waves of beach grass with gold. On the leeward side of the primary dune a less harsh environment increases the diversity of plant life found there. Here woody shrubs thrive, among them poison ivy (*Toxicodendron radicans*), bayberry (*Myrica pensylvanica*), and beach plum (*Prunus maritima*).

Between the primary and secondary dune lies the swale, a low-lying valley somewhat sheltered from saltspray but nevertheless another difficult environment for plants to thrive in. The swale sands often reach very high surface temperatures during the summer, especially in areas between small dunes where the sun's rays are magnified by reflection. Undisturbed areas of the swale are often blanketed with a prostrate evergreen mat of bearberry (*Arctostaphylos uva-ursi*), a small woody shrub with dark green leathery leaves and plump red berries in late summer. Resembling cranberries, the tempting edible berries are in fact quite bad tasting and even wildlife resort to them only as a winter starvation food after other food sources have been exhausted. Bearberry is the dominant plant in the swales of Fire Island, occupying more than 23 percent of the available area.

Blowouts and other disturbed dune and swale areas that are not attractive to beach grass are first colonized by beach heather (*Hud-*

The piping plover (*Charadrius melodus*) is a small shorebird whose breeding requirements restrict it to white sand beaches. This federally recognized endangered species reaches its highest known breeding concentrations on Long Island. This is a female incubating a clutch of eggs at Jones Beach State Park.

sonia tomentosa), which often forms sizable mats. Beach heather is another ground-hugging plant with tiny overlapping scalelike leaves clinging close to its numerous stems. In late May and early June, little yellow flowers smother the heather's muted teal green leaves in a showy floral display.

As we move through the swale toward the secondary dune, a more diverse collection of plants can be found, including some tree species that mark the transition from the dune/swale community to the maritime forest. On the beachward slope of the secondary dune we find pitch pine *(Pinus rigida),* red cedar *(Juniperus virginiana),* black cherry *(Prunus serotina),* and winged sumac *(Rhus copallina).* Because growing conditions are not optimum here, many of these plants take on atypical forms. Pitch pine reaches heights of fifty to sixty feet in Long Island's pine barrens but due to the caustic effects of salt spray, pitch pine in the swales of Fire Island may only reach heights of four to six feet. Trees in the swale have the look of bonsai: they seem stunted and gnarled, with curious crowns of numerous branches abruptly clipped flat at the top by the wind.

Besides the various water birds, the dune/swale community is home to a number of interesting creatures, each superbly adapted for life in this taxing environment. Various highly specialized insects thrive in the sands, such as the seaside grasshopper *(Trimerotropis maritima)* whose pale color renders it almost invisible on the dunes, and the sand-colored dune wolf spider *(Geolycosa pikei),* which rarely leaves its silk-lined burrow, where it waits at the entrance for an unsuspecting

"meal" to pass by. Intimately linked with the dunes is the life cycle of the eastern sand wasp *(Bembix americana spinolae).* The female has curved front legs with rigid hairs that make them especially useful as little shovels. She feverishly digs in the sand, stopping at times to hover in the air when she gets overheated. The process continues until the burrow is sufficiently deep beneath the surface so that the temperature remains cool. In the burrow she deposits a fly that she has caught, paralyzed, and laid an egg in, and seals the chamber. When the egg hatches, the larva has an instant food supply in the fly, but the wasp must feed the developing larva several more times. The wasp memorizes the location of the sealed chamber by familiar landmarks, such as plants, shells, patterns of beach grass, and so forth. If the visual clues become altered the wasp will fail to locate its burrow.

Among other creatures that can be found in the dune/swale habitat, the most spectacular are the monarch butterflies *(Danaus plexippus).* Large and showy, these orange-winged beauties appear in mid-September by the thousands as they congregate along the barrier islands while migrating south to their wintering grounds in the mountains of Mexico. At dusk they gather in large numbers on the leeward side of trees and shrubs, where they huddle together in tight, motionless masses for warmth and protection during the cool autumn evenings. When re-animated by the warming rays of morning's light, they rise to the skies in clouds. If you're lucky enough to hit it right, usually on a September morning after a cold front from the north passes, you may find thousands of monarchs flying about the dunes at Sunken Forest.

The painted lady *(Vanessa cardui)* is one of Long Island's and the world's most common butterflies, with a distribution that spans at least four continents, accounting for its other name of cosmopolitan lady. On Long Island it is found wherever sunshine and wildflowers are plentiful. The larva feed primarily on thistles *(Crisium spp.)* but will utilize other members of the composite family as well. This individual was photographed nectaring on spotted Joe Pye weed *(Eupatorium maculatum),* a late summer wildflower, growing in a wet area near Jones Beach State Park.

Fowler's toads (*Bufo woodhou-sei fowleri*) are the most conspicu-ous amphibian of the barrier islands. They hide during the heat of day beneath logs, bushes, or leaf litter and forage at night after the desiccating sun has set. In May and June, the toads mate and deposit their eggs in the bogs and temporary pools of water that often form between dunes. At dusk the male toads' distinctive calls—imagine the bleat of a sick sheep—echo through the dunes as they compete for mates. The small tad-poles metamorphose into minia-ture adults in a matter of weeks, and at times the young depart the ponds in such great numbers that the ground itself appears to be moving. One summer evening at Jones Beach I watched as hun-dreds of laughing gulls (*Larus atricilla*) took advantage of just such a mass exodus by voraciously feasting on the helpless toads as they emerged from their ponds.

Among the matted dune grass-es you may observe narrow run-ways an inch or two wide. These are the trails of the meadow vole (*Microtus pennsylvanicus*), a small mouse-sized rodent with long brownish fur and a short tail. These vegetarians are active diur-nally as well as nocturnally, feed-ing on grasses, sedges, seeds, and bark. Meadow voles reproduce throughout the year at astonish-ing rates and serve as a food sup-ply for the barrier islands' predators. The red fox (*Vulpes fulva*) hunting the dunes at night is particularly fond of them, as are the northern harriers (*Circus cya-neus*), hawks that patrol the dunes by day.

Beyond the crest of the sec-ondary dune in its leeward shadow conditions are sometimes suitable for the existence of a maritime

A snowy owl (*Nyctea acandiaca*) roosting at the top of a seaside dune at Jones Beach State Park. Snowy owls are Arctic breeding birds that occasionally winter along Long Island's barrier beaches, which are not unlike the Arctic tundra where the owls breed.

Northern saw-whet owls (*Aegolius acadicus*) are small owls (only eight inches long) but are just as efficient predators as their much larger cousins, the great horned owls. Saw-whets breed to the north of Long Island but beginning every November they arrive here to winter. They seem to favor plant-ings of pines and other ever-greens along the barrier islands for roosting during the day. This saw-whet was photographed in a red cedar at Jamaica Bay Wildlife Refuge.

forest. Maritime forests consist of some of the same deciduous and evergreen species found on mainland Long Island, but their growth patterns are quite different from mainland forests. Salt-laden winds passing over the secondary dune act like a hedge trimmer, neatly pruning the tops of trees. The resulting canopy is very dense, allowing little light to penetrate to the ground below. The shade- and salt-tolerant American holly (*Ilex opaca*) seems better able to tolerate these conditions than other species, hence its dominance in the Sunken Forest, the most impressive maritime forest on Long Island. Sassafras (*Sassafras albidum*), juneberry (*Amelanchier canadensis*), and black tupelo (*Nyssa sylvatica*) are the next most numerous tree species here.

The trees' lower trunks are usually straight, but they become more twisted and gnarled as they approach the forest canopy and its deforming winds. The species that survive in this habitat happen to have very distinctive bark: the ocher colored bark of the sassafras tree is furrowed; the juneberry has smooth, steel gray bark occasionally marked with vertical slashes; and the American holly's smooth bark has a shiny golden color. The textures and colors combined in twisted masses of trunks give this forest its special character.

Maritime forests on Long Island's barrier islands often have freshwater bogs and swamps in depressed areas where the water table reaches the surface. Their water source is a freshwater lens

under the surface of the island that floats on top of denser seawater below and can only be replenished with rainwater, so the condition of the bogs and swamps may change drastically from year to year depending upon annual precipitation. Fire Island has a variety of boggy depressions, from areas that are waterlogged for long periods of time to others that are wetter or drier from month to month; some are heavy with a buildup of organic material while others are largely composed of wet sand.

In the Sunken Forest, the sunnier boggy spots have luxuriant colonies of marsh fern (*Thelypteris palustris*) accompanied by the pinkish flowers of marsh Saint John's wort (*Hypericum virginicum*) in late summer. The bog margins also host high bush blueberry (*Vaccinium corymbosum*), whose sweet summer fruit is as popular with the wildlife as it is with pie pickers. The dominant tree in the Sunken Forest's wet areas is the black tupelo, but in several spots red maple (*Acer rubrum*) flourishes as well.

The maritime forests are home to many species of wildlife. The trees are alive with birds. Because of their geographic position, the barrier islands act as traps for migrating birds on the east coast of North America, making the islands a birder's paradise. (From September through October, the Sunken Forest is an excellent place to look for migrating hawks, and on good flight days, literally thousands of hawks of various species can be observed passing over the dunes.) Most of the larger animals present on the mainland live on

the barrier islands as well. On Fire Island the most notable animal denizen must be the white-tailed deer (*Odocoileus virginianus*). When the Sunken Forest was first opened to the public more than twenty years ago by the National Park Service, the deer population on Fire Island is thought to have been as low as fifty individuals; today the number is somewhere around five hundred. As there is no natural predator to check their expanding numbers, deer have greatly altered the environment through their overbrowsing of plants. The deer's association with the northern deer tick (*Ixodes daminii*), the carrier of Lyme disease, which, when left untreated, can have serious consequences for its human victims, has made their presence on the barrier islands an issue of public health. The incidence of Lyme disease on Long Island is very high, with Fire Island having one of the highest occurrence rates.

The sand apron that supports the maritime forest eventually tapers off into the comparatively gentle waters of the lagoons separating them from the mainland. These waters are considerably calmer than the Atlantic, and in their margins an entirely different community of life than the littoral has evolved: the salt marsh. The salt marshes along the barrier islands' northern edge and the marshes among Long Island's many lagoons, bays, harbors, and estuaries are places of great biological complexity and importance.

Long Island's barrier beaches put on an autumn display of color just as intense as that seen in the upland woods. Poison ivy (*Toxicodendron radicans*) turns a brilliant flame red in autumn. The green bushes in the background are bayberry (*Myrica pensylvanica*), and the white blossoms are actually the seed heads of groundsel bush (*Baccharis halimifolia*), also called sea myrtle because it thrives where salt concentrations in the groundwater are high.

American holly *(Ilex opaca)* is an attractive evergreen tree with smooth bark, pointed waxy green leaves, and bright red berries in autumn. Some of these trees in Fire Island's Sunken Forest are more than one hundred years old.

Beach plums *(Prunus maritima)* along Long Island's barrier beaches are covered by creamy white flowers in May. By November, their small purple fruits ripen, to be enjoyed by wildlife and humans alike.

A small freshwater pond
on the barrier island at the
John F. Kennedy Memorial Bird
Sanctuary near Tobay Beach
County Park, Nassau.

Opposite:
During wet years, some interdune swales fill with water.
One year this small pond among
the dunes at Jones Beach's
west end became a summer
home for muskrats *(Ondatra
zibethicus)* and Fowler's toads
(Bufo woodhousei fowleri).

CHAPTER 3

BAYS, LAGOONS, AND SALT MARSHES

The shallow lagoons between the barrier islands and the South Shore of Long Island include Jamaica Bay, South Oyster Bay, Great South Bay, Moriches Bay, and Shinnecock Bay. The Great South Bay is the largest of them and, at little more than five thousand years old, is among Long Island's most youthful geographic features. It is a striking example of a bar-built estuary formed when a rising postglacial sea was trapped between an indentation in Long Island and a barrier island. (An estuary is a partially enclosed body of seawater diluted by freshwater runoff from land. Estuaries are important coastal habitats since they support a greater diversity of organisms than the open sea.) The forces that created the bay are still at work, and it is estimated that the youthful bay's remaining lifetime is scarcely more than three thousand years.

Its eventual demise will be caused by sediment deposition and the landward-bound migration of Fire Island, which shields it from the Atlantic Ocean. During its brief life the bay has had a profound influence on Long Island and the surrounding coastal regions.

Given its proximity to the ocean, the Great South Bay is surprisingly placid. It is approximately twenty-five miles long and varies in width from only 328 yards near Smith Point to 6.8 miles at its widest near Bayshore. Because the three inlets that connect it to the sea—Fire Island, Jones, and Moriches—are extremely narrow, daily tidal variations of less than one foot characterize the bay, compared to the three-foot-high tides that wash the barrier islands' ocean beaches. These modest tides are favorable to suspension feeding organisms (creatures that filter particles of food from the water) and also conducive to salt marsh vegetative growth. The bay's shallow waters (average depth is approximately six and a half feet) are well lit by the sun, resulting in an abundance of primary producers (photosynthetic organisms that include algae, phytoplankton, and plants) comprising the base of a complex food web.

The bay receives relatively modest amounts of freshwater from a few feeble streams and rivers that run into it, but groundwater seeps directly into it from underground aquifers (great stores of groundwater trapped within the sandy sediments of Long Island). The freshwater intrusion lowers the salinity, creating an estuarylike habitat. The streams and rivers also carry fine-grained sediments and nutrients from decaying plants that provide a substrate for marsh development and a nutrient source for the bay's primary producers.

The Great South Bay is considered one of the continent's most productive marine habitats. Marine scientists define production as the amount of carbon dioxide fixed by photosynthetic organisms per unit of time. The fixing of carbon by primary producers such as phytoplankton, algae, and plants ensures a nurturing food reserve for the bay's other organisms. Phytoplankton are small creatures, ranging in size from microscopic to a millimeter or so across, suspended in the water close to the surface. Although they are technically not plants (even though phytoplankton is a Greek word meaning "wandering plants") but members of the protist kingdom, they perform photosynthesis as plants do, using sunlight, carbon dioxide, water, and nutrients to grow and release oxygen. Phytoplankton can be tiny free-floating organisms, such as diatoms, or may occur as colonial clusters of algae cells. All marine life depends on the oxygen they release and they are important food sources for many small herbivores as well. Zooplankton are a varied class of small and microscopic animals that feeds on phytoplankton, bacteria, and other zooplankton. Some zooplankton, such as copepods and amphipods, spend their entire lives as zooplankton. Other marine animals use a zooplankton stage as only a part of their overall life cycle. Many species of barnacles, crabs, mollusks, and finfish have larval stages classified as zooplankton.

Seaweed, which is abundant in the bay, is comprised of another group of primary producers, called macroalgae, also classified in the protist kingdom. Some of the various species of macroalgae that inhabit Long Island's waters are anchored to the bay floor by strong rootlike holdfasts, while others are free floating. Green algae (*Chlorophyta*), brown algae (*Phaeophyta*), and red algae (*Rhodophyta*) are three phyla of seaweed, each represented by a number of individual species, found in our area. Sea lettuce (*Ulva lactuca*) is a green seaweed commonly found along Long Island's shores that strongly resembles its supermarket namesake, with a translucent sheetlike thallus (as the leaflike part of a seaweed is called) that has lobed or ruffled edges. It grows in a variety of places, from stagnant brackish pools to shallow well-lit water, and can thrive in moderately polluted conditions. Green fleece (*Codium fragile*) is another common green seaweed of the Great South Bay and other Long Island waters. It is a nonnative species accidentally introduced from Europe in 1957 and now well established in Long Island's bays. When washed ashore it resembles a knotted mass of velvety green cord often firmly attached by its holdfast to a substrate of shells or pebbles.

The only true green plant growing in Long Island's bays is eel grass (*Zostera marina*). Eel grass is an angiosperm (that is, a flowering plant) that evolved on land but eventually colonized marine habitats. It is the only flowering plant in our region that produces pollen and sets seed under sea water. Eel grass relies on currents to distribute its pollen the way grasses above water use the wind. The shallow, still waters of Long Island's sheltered bays are home to great underwater grasslands of this unusual plant. The Great South Bay has large eel-grass beds, and much of the bay's shoreline is blanketed with dead broken pieces of it. At times the north shore of Fire Island is ankle deep in winding bands of brown eel

Seaweed is often broken from its substrate of shells or rocks by wave action and deposited along the shores with the tide. This ropelike thallus of green fleece (*Codium fragile*), found along the shoreline of the Little Peconic Bay, is still attached by its holdfast to a substrate of shells.

The shells of two Atlantic jackknife clams (*Ensis directus*) are illuminated by sunset light on a mud flat at low tide. Jackknife clams are common although seldom seen bivalves in the Great South Bay.

Opposite:
The falling tide exposes an emerald green band of sea lettuce (*Ulva lactuca*), a common seaweed in Long Island's bays and still, brackish waters. This is Block Island Sound.

grass drying in the summer sun. During the Colonial era people collected, washed, and redried the grass, using it as a comfortable mattress stuffing, but today—with the exception of a few gardeners on the barrier islands who use it for mulch—only birds and other animals exploit the eel-grass wrack, searching for a crab, insect, amphipod, or the other edible treasures it harbors.

The eel-grass beds of the Great South Bay are one of the primary reasons why that region is such a productive marine habitat. Decaying bits of dead eel grass become part of the detritus (dead organic matter) food chain as they are transformed by bacteria and other microorganisms into an important nutrient source for higher organisms. The dense eel-grass beds act as a nursery for the young of many marine creatures, providing both shelter and food.

The larva and seed of the hard clam (*Mercenaria mercenaria*), also called the northern quahog, find food and shelter from predators within these beds. Conditions are so favorable that between 1970 and 1978 the Great South Bay led the nation in the harvesting of hard clams. Unfortunately, since that time overharvesting, degradation of water quality, and, possibly, natural population fluctuations have reduced their numbers. Another shellfish of economic importance in our bays is the bay scallop (*Aequipecten irradians*). Bay scallops live just below the intertidal zone, resting on the bottom of the bay where they suspension feed, but their young attach themselves to eel grass using byssal threads. An adult scallop when startled can rapidly propel itself away from danger by clapping its shells and expelling a jet stream of water, and they are

unusual in being such a mobile member of the bivalve family. The Atlantic jackknife clam (*Ensis directus*) is another bivalve that lives in sandy sediments, but being more characteristic of its family it moves slowly along the bay floor. As its shell does not close completely at the ends, it relies on burrowing for protection from predators. Jackknifes are among the most beautiful and unusually shaped bivalves in our waters. Their shells are commonly found on beaches but living animals are rarely encountered.

The eel grass forms a prairielike grassland underwater but, where the bay is shallow and calm, above its surface emerges another marine grassland of equal ecological importance, the salt marsh.

The salt marsh is among the most misunderstood and maligned of the world's various ecosystems. Historically salt marshes have been regarded as waste areas that offer little more than disease-carrying mosquitoes and foul organic odors, and only recently has their importance been recognized. Salt marshes are found in quiet bays, harbors, lagoons, and estuaries, in areas where human activities often lead to their elimination, either directly by land filling or indirectly by draining and the introduction of pollutants. It appears, however, that such environmental problems as the decline of finfish and shellfish populations and more frequent flooding of low-lying land are among the symptoms of a sick or undersized salt marsh community.

Viewed from above, a salt marsh reveals its intricate structure and balance. From this perspective, one can see the complex drainage patterns formed by winding tidal streams and the subtle colors that distinguish the varieties of salt marsh flora. These species closely coexist, each occu-

pying a specific microhabitat often defined by no more than a subtle change (an inch or so) in elevation. Seen up close, the salt marsh reveals the numerous organisms—including mussels, snails, worms, insects, and birds—that live within the sea of grass. Salt marshes are one of the most productive habitats on Earth. With the exception of sugarcane, there is no cultivated crop that exceeds the production of organic nutrients produced by a salt marsh. Remarkably a salt marsh accomplishes this without the fertilizers and other special care provided by farmers. Salt marshes along with the eel grass beds provide the foundation for the great diversity and numbers of marine organisms within Long Island's bays.

The summer salt marsh is a sea of emerald green grass, a Midwestern prairie emerging from the waters of a still bay. The sounds of the salt marsh are equally inviting. The songs of birds fill the air as the wind rustles the grasses and the rising and ebbing tides bubble and gurgle over the marsh's thick sediments. In autumn the brilliant green of summer changes to a taupe brown that when illuminated by the setting sun shines with a characteristic golden hue. This seemingly uncomplicated environment is a complex association of many plants and animals that exist under a dictum of exacting requirements.

What makes a salt marsh? Streams along Long Island's South Shore carry fine-grained, nutrient-rich, particulate matter into the bays. Over the years, deposits form in the quiet waters with their relatively level bottoms. As these mucky, organic sediments approach the surface, various algal pioneers invade, soon to be followed by the marsh's dominant plant, tall marsh cordgrass (*Sparti-*

na alterniflora). (The common name cordgrass describes its use by early inhabitants as a source of fiber for making cord and twine.) As the cordgrass grows, the developing plants stifle the surging tides, slowing down water currents and thereby encouraging the further deposition of sediments among their stems and roots. Marshes formed this way usually begin around the midtide level but, as the mucky substrate accumulates, they may be raised to the high tide mark. They never extend into deeper water, as the cordgrass, being a terrestrial plant that has invaded the sea, cannot stand prolonged submersion in salt water or the constant battering of wave action. The topography of the South Shore bays include many areas conducive to this form of salt marsh development and the gentle taper of the sand aprons along the northern shores of the barrier islands also gives rise to vast areas of salt marsh. Large marshes also develop in other calm, shallow regions throughout the bays. Many of Long Island's bays have large tracts of salt marsh unexpectedly in their interior sections that probably originated along sandbars in the shallow waters.

The ceaseless nature of the marsh building processes slowly mold the marshes so that their shape and location are continually changing. Within a human life span, it is not unusual for a marsh to become filled and choked by sediments or to succumb to open water. Storms affect the stability of a salt marsh as well. After the December nor'easter of 1992, for example, washovers and breaches in the barrier islands exposed marshes to turbulent water and smothering sands.

As a salt marsh develops, it forms intricate tidal creek patterns that drain the marsh when the tide ebbs and flood its furthest reaches when the sea returns. The tides nurture the flora and fauna of the marsh twice a day by depositing detritus as well as oxygenated water, minerals, and other nutrients. Now and then, the tides overflow the creeks, depositing sediments along their banks. These elevated regions support different plants than the relatively flat areas of the marsh: marsh elder *(Iva frutescens),* a rather tall shrub, is one example. Occasionally the winding creeks become so contorted that their twists and turns will reconnect, severing a portion of the creek and forming a horseshoe-shaped pool termed an oxbow. These stagnant pools support organisms quite different from the rest of the marsh.

Small round or oval pools of a different origin dot Long Island's marshes as well. When the tide recedes, water left standing in shallow muddy depressions evaporates quickly in the sun, leaving behind a salt-laden surface known as a salt pan. The plants associated with the pans are highly tolerant of extremely saline conditions and as a result the salt pans stand out from the rest of the marsh. Salt pans can be beautiful structures distinguished by concentric rings of vegetation with speciation differences apparent as the pan's circumference becomes reduced and its salt concentrations increase. During the summer, the green fleshy stalks of glasswort *(Salicornia virginica),* an extremely salt-tolerant species, can be seen around the salt pans and other areas of the high marsh. Glasswort is edible and its high salt content and crispy texture are reminiscent of pickles. It is quite a tasty plant and I occasionally see it for sale in farmer's markets in the metropolitan area. By autumn this inconspicuous plant rivals the most brilliant New England autumn foliage by itself turning an intense crimson red.

Plants of the salt marsh each have their own zones, with separation usually determined by a species tolerance to saline conditions and the degree of immersion in water it is able to tolerate. While the lowest zone of the marsh consists almost entirely of cordgrass, the further away you move from the water the greater the diversity of plants. The high marsh is a dense green meadow dominated by salt meadow grass, or salt hay (*Spartina patens*), which is not nearly as tall as the marsh cordgrass. As its name suggests, salt hay makes good fodder for cattle and horses. During the summer months when the sun is low, the salt hay is a brilliant emerald green tufted carpet spread across the marsh. Spike grass (*Distichlis spicata*) thrives in the uppermost portions of the marsh, infrequently visited by the tides. This plant is host to the salt marsh skipper (*Panoquina panoquin*), a small, nondescript butterfly restricted to the salt marsh community. Black grass (*Juncus gerardi*) usually occupies the zone above the spike grass. Its name is derived from its black fruit capsules born conspicuously from June to September. Black grass is not a true grass but a member of the rush family.

Scattered about the high marsh are a number of showy, flowering species of plants. During late summer, salt marsh aster (*Aster tenuifolius*) brightens the fading marsh with its pale lavender petals. The bright pink blooms of marsh pink (*Sabatia stellaris*) daintily dance over the high marsh in late summer as well. Certainly the most striking plant found in Long Island's marshes must be the swamp rose mallow (*Hibiscus palustris*). The rose mallow is a giant summer perennial reaching heights of five to seven feet with four- to seven-inch fiery pink blossoms to match. Swamp mallows are so stunning and uncharacteristic of this region that to stumble upon a group of these plants for the first time is to be transported to a tropical paradise.

Many species of photosynthetic algae live on the marsh mud amid these plants. Individually, they contribute little to the productivity of the salt marsh, but together the countless diatoms, dinoflagellates, and other protists make an enormous impact. Most of the organic material produced in a salt marsh (more than 90 percent) goes unused by the herbivores present and is eventually flushed into the open bay where it is consumed by other creatures.

Long Island's salt marshes are responsible for a great deal of the species diversity of its South Shore bays. The young of many finfish species reside in the marsh where food and shelter are abundant, until they are large enough to deal with the dangers of the open water. In spring almost any marsh on the island is home to great numbers of birds. Mornings will find the marsh filled with the loud, rattling notes of marsh wrens (*Cistothorus palustris*). These tiny, inconspicuous passerines (perching birds) are rarely seen as they flitter through the marsh grasses, but during the peak of the early summer breeding season their singing fills the air both day and night. Their nest is a curious football-shaped structure woven from grass and anchored to the marsh grass not far above the water's surface. Although a breeding pair will occupy only one nest, the male marsh wren feverishly builds several, apparently to prove his virility to a prospective mate or perhaps as a diversion for predators. Sharp-tailed sparrows (*Ammodramus caudacutus*) and seaside sparrows (*Ammodramus maritimus*) are two small passerines that also call the marsh home.

Slight differences in the breeding and feeding habits of these similar birds allow them to coexist. When twilight covers the summer marsh their buzzing songs can be clearly heard.

The willet (*Catoptrophorus semipalmatus*) is a large, noisy member of the sandpiper family with a striking black-and-white wing pattern. In contrast to the willet's conspicuous visual and cacophonous breeding displays, their nests remain well hidden within the depths of the marsh grass. Willets are widespread throughout Long Island's marshes, but the bird that is most closely associated with the salt marsh is the clapper rail (*Rallus longirostris*). The clapper rail is strictly a bird of the cordgrass, unlike the willet and other salt marsh breeders that can also be found on sandy beaches and other areas in proximity to the marsh. In its size, shape, and habits, it superficially resembles a domesticated chicken, accounting for its familiar name of marsh hen. Clappers are secretive

Willets (*Catoptrophorus semipalmatus*) are large shorebirds that breed in good numbers along Long Island's bays. This willet is searching for food, probably small insects and marine invertebrates, along the shoreline of the Great South Bay on Fire Island National Seashore.

Overleaf:
The salt marsh on Captree Island in the Great South Bay at sunrise.

Tall marsh cordgrass *(Spartina alterniflora)* borders the still margins of Little Bay in Orient Point State Park.

Opposite:
A winged sumac *(Rhus copallina)* in fall colors growing along the edge of Hallocks Bay, a small marsh-lined bay on Long Island's North Fork, near Orient.

The swamp rose mallow
(Hibiscus palustris) is one of
Long Island's showiest wildflowers. Its large pink flowers
have a tropical look to them
quite unlike anything else on
the island.

Left:
Tall marsh cordgrass *(Spartina
alterniflora)* is a common grass
of Long Island's salt marshes
that normally grows in those
parts of the marsh that are
flooded daily by the tides. As
its name suggests, this species
can reach heights of more
than six feet, depending upon
local conditions. Pictured here
is a small marsh on the Great
South Bay where the tall
marsh cordgrass is only a little
over a foot high.

Page 50:
Sea lavender *(Limonium car-
loinianum)* is a late-blooming
perennial of tidal marshes. It
has a basal set of broad leaves
that produces an intricate
branching cluster of tiny blue
flowers in late summer. The
higher margins of salt marshes
not subject to daily tidal flooding are home to a variety of
interesting wildflowers.

Page 51:
Glasswort *(Salicornia virginica)*
is an extremely salt-tolerant
plant that grows in the salt
pans of Long Island's coastal
margins. By October, its green
fleshy stems turn an intense
crimson red, rivaling the
autumn colors of Long Island's
woodlands.

The great blue heron (*Ardea herodias*), standing more than five feet tall, is the largest wading bird in the Long Island area. With its spear-like bill and whip action equipped neck, it patrols shallow water primarily for fish but also takes invertebrates, frogs, and rodents.

The black crowned night-heron (*Nycticorax nycticorax*) is a stocky bird with a bold black capped head and neck and striking white hindneck plumes. Pictured is a juvenile sporting a more subdued plumage. (It will attain mature plumage in its second year.) These birds are locally common along the island's coastal areas and, as their name suggests, are primarily nocturnal feeders.

birds seldom seen as they skulk through the cordgrass in search of food. Their conspicuous call of ten or more sharp staccato notes, rising then dropping in loudness and acceleration, is a telltale sign of their ubiquitous occupation of the marshes.

The northern harrier (*Circus cyaneus*), or marsh hawk, is a keen-eyed predator that patrols the marsh, lazily banking back and forth, often only inches above the cordgrass. Upon flushing a small bird, the harrier becomes an aerial acrobat, easily catching its evasive prey. Harriers also possess a developed sense of hearing that they use while searching for rodents hidden within the marsh grass. On Long Island, the harrier is considered threatened primarily due to a loss of breeding and feeding habitats; consequently harriers are not very common, especially during the summer breeding season. In winter, however, the harrier population rises, augmented by wintering birds from northern populations. The marshes around our barrier islands are particularly good places to observe them.

When the tide is low, the thick muddy substrate of the salt marsh reveals a host of creatures. Ribbed mussels (*Modiolus demissus*) live nestled between the stems of cordgrass, half buried in the mud and held firmly in place to pebbles and shells by byssal threads. Byssal, derived from the Greek word for "beard," aptly describes the array of organic threadlike projections secreted from the mussel's foot. The mussels are suspension feeders that take in and expel water through siphons while their gills play a dual role extracting oxygen and detrital food. Common mud snails (*Ilynassa obsoleta*) live on the muddy marsh bottom as well. Unlike the mussels, mud snails are mobile and often seen at low tide

patrolling the marsh and mud flats for food. They are opportunistic feeders that will scavenge a dead crab or fish or occasionally attack a living creature. Mud snails can easily clear a beach of decaying organic material.

The diamondback terrapin (*Malaclemys terrapin*) is a fairly large turtle that hunts for prey within the marshes and their tidal creeks. They occur in good numbers around Long Island despite their exploitation for turtle soup, and in early summer females can be observed emerging from the marsh when the tide is high to lay their eggs in warm sandy soil. Terrapins restrict themselves to the marshes and estuaries; snapping turtles (*Chelydra serpentina*), which are more common in fresh water, frequent the brackish marshes as well.

The muskrat (*Ondatra zibethicus*) is probably the most common larger mammal of the salt marshes around our bays. Members of the rodent family, they are plump-bodied and often two feet in length. A luxurious long-haired brown pelt covers all of the muskrat's body except for its long round tail (hence the "rat" part of its name). The muskrat's home is more often seen than the animal itself: it is a large structure resembling a tepee two to three feet in height and built of marsh grasses, usually in an area of shallow water. Muskrats also build feeding platforms that they use while dining on root stocks or occasionally small fish and invertebrates. At dusk when they are most active, look for a distinctive "V" in the water created as they swim with their heads held high.

Migratory species such as Arctic-bound shorebirds use the island's marshes as a wayside to rest and refuel before continuing their northward journey, while large numbers of breeding birds begin their yearly reproductive cycle there. There is no better place to observe migrating and breeding birds than the Jamaica Bay Wildlife Refuge at the western end of Long Island (it's actually within New York City limits). Jamaica Bay is a broad, shallow bay sheltered behind a barrier-beach complex with one opening to the sea. The bay originally contained more than twenty-five thousand acres of salt marsh and had an average depth of three feet. Today, approximately thirteen thousand acres remain, of which about nine thousand belong to the refuge, and dredging has deepened the average depth to sixteen feet.

Too many species stop here to list them all, but just about every shorebird species in eastern North America, as well as various exotics, makes an appearance in the fall. Some of the more common species, often present by the hundreds, include semipalmated plover *(Charadrius semipalmatus)*, dunlin *(Calidris alpina)*, semipalmated sandpiper *(Calidris pusilla)*, least sandpiper *(Calidris minutilla)*, greater yellowlegs *(Tringa melanoleuca)*, and lesser yellowlegs *(Tringa flavipes)*. Every year a small spattering of rarer shorebirds passes through. Some of these species include Baird's sandpiper *(Calidris bairdii)*, buff breasted sandpiper *(Tryngites subruficollis)*, and lesser golden plover *(Pluvialis dominica)*. Recently, the circumpolar spotted redshank *(Tringa erythropus)* and the sharptailed sandpiper *(Calidris acuminata)* from Asia have been observed. There are usually good numbers of brant geese *(Branta bernicla)* in the bay, but their beauty is overshadowed by the flocks of wintering snow geese *(Chen caerulescens)* arriving from their Arctic breeding grounds. Snow

Dunlins *(Calidris alpina)* are colorful little shorebirds that breed in the high Arctic but use Long Island's barrier beaches as an important resting and feeding stop on their long migratory journey. Each year a small number of dunlins winter along the barrier beaches as well.

Snowy egrets *(Egretta thula)* spend a good deal of time roosting and preening. Preening removes parasites and cleans feathers, keeping them in top condition for both flight and insulation. Between preening sessions, snowy egrets become voracious feeders at the water's edge. Their diets are diverse and I have seen them eat creatures as small as flies and as large as bullfrogs. During the spring, summer, and fall, snowy egrets are common throughout Long Island in the vicinity of both fresh and salt water.

Semipalmated plovers *(Charadrius semipalmatus)* are migratory shorebirds that breed in the high Arctic. They use Long Island's beaches as a wayside for rest and food each year on their migration to and from their wintering grounds in the southern United States, Central America, and South America. This individual is bathing, a necessary and frequent activity that helps keep its flight feathers in prime condition.

Migrating snow geese
(Chen caerulescens) fly
over the barrier island
beach at Jones Beach
State Park early one
autumn morning.

The short-billed dowitcher
(Limnodromus griseus) is just
one of the thirty or so different
species of shorebirds that stop
by the Jamaica Bay Wildlife
Refuge as a feeding and resting
station on their way to and
from their southern wintering
grounds. Short-billed dowitch-
ers that pass through Long
Island breed in nothern Quebec
and Labrador and winter anywhere from Florida through the
Caribbean to points as far
south as Brazil.

geese are pure white except for black-tipped wings and fit into the winter landscape as if they were made of snow and ice. In the morning, there is usually a flock of snow geese on the West Pond.

The parade of shorebirds attracts their primary predators, the merlin *(Falco tinnunculus)* and peregrine falcon *(Falco peregrinus)*, which especially enjoys the tender flesh of a plump plover. The area is so attractive that a pair of peregrines has bred successfully for the last several years on the nearby Marine Park Bridge. Recently the osprey has joined the ranks of breeding birds of prey in Jamaica Bay. A pair fledged young for the first time in the history of New York City during the summer of 1992; as of 1996 three breeding pairs are in the bay. The fall and winter are particularly good times to find hawks and owls in the refuge. Rarities such as northern goshawk *(Accipiter gentilis)* and rough-legged hawk *(Buteo lagopus)* appear most years. Saw-whet owls *(Aegolius acadicus)* and short-eared owls *(Asio flammeus)* are common winter residents, and the refuge also contains the metropolitan area's largest concentration of breeding barn owls, thanks to a rigorous program involving the strategic deployment of nesting boxes. Within the city, rodents are almost at infinite supply, and now, with the proper housing, the owls have flourished.

The spring migration brings fewer shorebirds, hawks, and waterfowl than in fall, but it does produce an abundance of songbirds. Songbirds migrating from the South find Jamaica Bay as the first landfall after their exhausting journey across the ocean. Small trees and shrubs are ideal for morning viewing of tired warblers after an evening flight. Most migrating songbirds use the

Diamondback terrapins *(Malaclemys terrapin)* are turtles of the island's bays and tidal creeks. They are fully aquatic, but in June the females come to shore to lay their eggs in warm sandy soil.

evenings to fly, feeding and resting during the day. On spring "wave days," when vast numbers of songbirds descend on the refuge, the sight and sound of calling birds is spectacular.

One of the most significant changes to Long Island's bays has been levied over the years by the reduction of salt marsh habitat. The dredging of channels, like Jones Inlet, has facilitated the demise of salt marshes by increasing the turbidity and raising the level of water within the bay. The building of bulkheads and the draining and filling of marshes have also reduced their acreage. Today, thanks to recognition of the value of the salt marshes and their importance to the entire bay, laws have been enacted that curtail most of this activity, yet other threats remain, particularly from coastal development and runoff from streets and sewers. The consequence is a reduction in population numbers for various species of organisms as well as in the diversity of species found in the bay today.

Muskrats *(Ondatra zibethicus)* are common mammals in Long Island's salt marshes. Although they are primarily vegetarians, this one seems to be enjoying the arm of a sea star it fished out of a tidal pool in Montauk State Park.

CHAPTER 4

THE NORTH SHORE AND
THE LONG ISLAND SOUND

The Long Island Sound forms the picturesque northern shoreline of Long Island. A long, narrow body of sheltered water that fills the void of land between Long Island to the south and the mainland to the north, the sound is approximately twenty-one miles across at its widest. On a clear day Connecticut is clearly visible from many North Shore beaches. From New York City the sound stretches eastward 110 miles to Orient Point, at the tip of Long Island's North Fork. Unlike the South Shore bays, which are really lagoons, it is a fairly deep body of water, with an average depth of sixty-five feet and a maximum depth of 350 feet.

A primordial Long Island Sound appeared between eleven thousand and twenty-two thousand years ago as continental glaciation waned in a warming world climate. Meltwater from glaciers filled the deep canyon between the Connecticut hills and the land that was to become Long Island. The Harbor Hill Moraine, a sinuous terminal mound of gravel, clay, and sand deposited by the receding ice sheets, served as the southern boundary for this growing lake.

The melting glaciers filled the infant sound with cool, fresh water and deposited a layer of sediment roughly five hundred feet thick beneath its surface. This "proto-sound" persisted for several thousand years as a glacial lake with no link to the sea. The lake eventually overflowed the Harbor Hill Moraine and cut a deep channel at its eastern end that drained most of its water, once again leaving a deep basin between the Connecticut hills and what would become Long Island. Close to eight thousand years ago the continued worldwide melting of glaciers caused an abrupt rise in sea level, and seawater flowed into the basin from the east. As the sea level continued to rise, a second opening formed to the west near New York City. The present-day sound began to mature about forty-five hundred years ago, when sea level and climate stabilized to current conditions. Now the sound and its Long Island shores were stable enough for colonization by a variety of organisms.

The Long Island Sound is an estuary. Estuaries are partially enclosed coastal bodies of water where the salt-laden water of the sea meets and mixes with fresh water. The numerous small streams and rivers that flow into the sound along with showers and groundwater seepage account for its freshwater content. The Connecticut River is by far the major contributor, with a watershed that includes much of New England and extends as far north as Canada. On the Long Island side, the Nissequogue River lazily enters the sound at Sunken Meadow State Park. Several small streams and creeks along the North Shore make minor freshwater additions as well. Along the base of the gravel and clay cliffs on the North Shore one can often see groundwater slowly trickling toward the surf. Salty ocean water reaches the sound at its eastern end through the Race, a narrow inlet of strong currents that have etched a channel, creating the sound's deepest point of 350 feet.

Estuaries are important ecosystems in that they are rich in food and nutrients and offer protected havens for young marine life. Long Island Sound is no exception. Along with its pelagic (open water) and benthic (seafloor) portions, it creates a diversity of habitats along the island's shoreline, including sheltered harbors, salt marshes, tidal flats, rocky intertidal zones, and sandy beaches. As in all natural bodies of water, plants, algae, and other chlorophyll-containing organisms are the basis for the complex chain of life that the sound supports, but an overabundance of certain species can have devastating consequences on the local ecology. So-called "red tides," for example, occur when dinoflagellates, which are species of red phytoplankton, release toxins fatal to marine life. A different kind of crisis can occur during times of excessive phytoplankton growth: as dead and decaying algae monopolize the available oxygen in the process of decomposing, oxygen needed by animals is depleted and a condition called "hypoxia" results. From 1987 through 1989, the sound experienced such a phytoplankton bloom, causing grave results for many marine inhabitants. The recent upsurge in phytoplankton blooms (dubbed "brown tides") has been attributed to increasing levels of soluble nitrogen (an essential nutrient for phytoplankton) in the sound. Sewage treatment plants, along with air pollution and other nonpoint pollutants, are the major sources of excess nitrogen in the sound. (A nonpoint pollutant is a chemical that cannot be traced to a specific place.)

Among the macroalgaes, sea lettuce (*Ulva lactuca*) is especially common on the North Shore. At low tide, it lies matted over the rocks and pebbles, imparting an emerald green color to the beach. There are several species of brown seaweeds, called rockweeds (*Fucus spp.*), found along the sound's shore. *Fucus vesiculosus* anchors itself in shallow water using holdfasts. It is the only rockweed in our area with air bladders along its thallus: these hold the three-foot-long fronds upright in the water so that they are better exposed to nutrients and light. Like bubble wrap, they're fun to pop. The only true plant that grows in the open water of the sound is eel grass (*Zostera marina*), which migrating and wintering waterfowl, especially Brant geese (*Branta bernicla*), depend on as a primary food source. As in the South Shore bays, eel-grass beds in shallow areas serve as nurseries for young finfish, shellfish, and other marine life, providing both food and cover, while cordgrasses are the primary plants of the North Shore salt marshes. The North Shore has fewer sheltered areas of calm, shallow water than the South Shore, and consequently its salt marshes are small and usually nestled in the nooks and crannies of its rugged harbors. There are also tracts of salt marshes hidden in the shelter of sand spits and along the mouths of rivers, particularly the Nissequogue River and the Wading River. The salt marsh at the head of Cold Spring Harbor is typical of the North Shore. It is a true estuary, with a small stream and springs feeding it fresh water, and salty tides flooding it twice daily. It has a drier upper region dominated by salt meadow grass and a lower region of tall marsh cordgrass. Its extensive mud flats, uncovered at low tide, are especially attractive in spring and again in late summer to migrating shorebirds, such as semipalmated plovers (*Charadrius semipalmatus*), semipalmated sandpipers (*Calidris pusilla*), greater yellowlegs (*Tringa melanoleuca*), and others that feed on the multitude of tiny invertebrates hidden within the mud.

The sound has a rich and diverse finfish population. Some species of fish are year-round residents while others are migratory, inhabiting the sound at a specific time each year. Among the former are the winter flounder (*Pseudopleuronectes americanus*), which prefer the cool deep waters of the sound in summer. When water temperature drops in the autumn, they move into the shallow bays to spawn. While young, winter flounder have an eye on each side of their bodies, as one might expect. As they grow, the left eye migrates to the right side of the head, and the flat adults swim with their left side (now their bottom side) down and their two eyes on their right side above. They lurk in the bottoms of bays feeding on benthic (that is, bottom dwelling) creatures. Winter flounder have a

chameleonlike ability to change the color of their scales to match their surroundings. Windowpane flounder (*Scophthalmus aquosus*)– which resemble the winter flounder but with both eyes on the left side, not the right–are also abundant in the sound. Other common year-round residents include the mummichog (*Fundulus heteroclitus*) and four-spined stickleback (*Apeltes quadracus*), two small fish that both prefer inshore brackish areas. Atlantic silversides (*Menidia menidia*) are small schooling fish fond of the sandy seashores and mouths of inlets. Blackfish (*Tautoga onitis*) are year-round residents that during the warmer months feed on mollusks and barnacles in rocky areas close to shore. When winter comes and the water temperature drops, they move into deeper water, where they remain in an inactive phase in the shelter of rocky crevices.

Along with the flounder, the little skate (*Raja erinacea*) is one of the most abundant finfish species in Long Island Sound. Little skates have enlarged pectoral fins fused to their heads, giving their bodies a disklike shape. Like sharks, skates have a cartilaginous skeleton, fertilization is internal, and the males have a modified pelvic fin that forms a copulatory organ called the clasper. The little skate's clasper is one of the largest known copulatory organs for an animal relative to its size. Little skates lay black, leathery egg cases several inches long. They are rectangular with four horny protrusions, one at each corner, and resemble a small pouch, hence their common name, the mermaid's purse. They wash up on shore after storms; carefully opening one will often reveal a skate embryo at some point in its development.

Anadromous fish are species that migrate from the ocean's salt water to freshwater rivers and

streams, where they spawn. Several species of anadromous fish migrate into the sound each year to spawn in its tributaries. Before the sound's shores were intensely developed for human habitation, great numbers of Atlantic salmon (*Salmo salar*) entered the sound. By the mid-1800s, overfishing, pollution, and habitat destruction (primarily damned rivers) led to the local extinction of salmon. Despite efforts to restore populations, such as ladders for migrating fish to clear dams, the salmon population in the sound remains far below their historical numbers. Striped bass (*Morone saxatilis*) are large fish (up to six feet) with seven to eight black stripes running down their sides. In the Long Island region they spawn primarily in the Hudson River and do not use any of the Long Island Sound tributaries. Nevertheless they are present in the sound in good numbers. They are fierce predators of smaller fish that arrive in early spring and feed in shallow water close to Long Island's shores before departing in autumn. A small number of striped bass probably overwinter in the sound as well.

American shad (*Alosa sapidissima*), a member of the herring family, is another anadromous fish that had the same fate as the Atlantic salmon. Today the Connecticut River is the only Long Island Sound tributary with a major shad run. Shad get their name from shadbush (*Amelanchier spp.*), which includes several different species of shrublike trees of the Long Island region. Shadbush are members of the rose family that have white, five-petaled flowers that burst into bloom before their leaves appear in early April. This coincides with the arrival of spawning American shad. Early settlers to the region gave shad bush other names evocative of their daily lives: Juneberry, for its small, reddish-black fruits that ripen in early summer and were used in jams, jellies, and pies, and serviceberry, because its early spring bloom occurs around the same time that Colonial preachers would begin delivering sermons to outlying rural communities after winter's isolation.

The alewife (Alosa pseudoharengus), like the shad, is a small (about a foot long) member of the herring family. These silvery fish with greenish backs and large black eyes have small dark shoulder spots on their sides that make them easy to identify. Unlike shad, they still make spawning runs each spring into several of Long Island's small streams. In mid-April, adult alewives begin to move from the ocean into shallow coastal waters near the streams and creeks where they were born several years previously. Researchers do not fully understand the navigational mechanism they employ, but, as with other anadromous fish, it is believed that an olfactory sense directs them to the natal streams where they were born. They actually "smell" the distinct odor of their point of origin. Females lay as many as a quarter of a million eggs each, but by early fall, when the young alewives return to the sea, their numbers are not nearly as great. A long line of predators from bullfrogs to herons preys on the young. Humans, of course, are more discerning than wildlife and do not favor the bony alewives for a meal. Native Americans and early settlers caught thousands of these fish each spring for another purpose, however: farmers would spread alewives across their fields, where their decaying carcasses

provided a cheap and plentiful organic fertilizer. Before long, overharvesting reduced the alewife population drastically, and, by the early 1700s, laws were enacted across the east coast to protect the runs. Presently on Long Island, alewife runs are limited to a handful of streams.

American eels (Anquilla rostrata) are snakelike catadromous fishes. Catadromous fish spend most of their adult lives in fresh water and migrate to salt water to spawn, the exact opposite behavior of the anadromous fish. The larger females are about three feet long, with the males being slightly smaller. They are nocturnal scavengers that will eat just about anything, dead or alive. Adult eels leave Long Island's streams and rivers, entering the sound in winter and early spring. They migrate south to the Sargasso Sea, just southwest of Bermuda, where they mate and die. The eggs hatch into ribbonlike transparent larvae called leptocephalus that are quite unlike the adults. Within a year the larvae begin a migration back to the North American streams that their parents left the previous year, where they live as adults for three or four more years before the cycle begins again. The mechanism of this migration is a mystery.

The Long Island Sound harbors other creatures besides finfish. Harbor seals (Phoca vitulina) and gray seals (Halichoerus grypus) are the only marine mammals that occur within Long Island Sound with any regularity. They are most frequently spotted in the winter months, either hauled out on rocks at low tide or bobbing along the shore in search of food. Their numbers have been increasing over the years, and they have recently been spotted as far west as Hempstead Harbor. Harbor por-

poises (Phocoena phocoena) were at one time common in the sound, but today it would be unusual to see one. Other whales and dolphins make infrequent visits, but every so often a surprising sighting occurs. Beluga whales (Delphinapterus leucas), those ghostly white, torpedo-shaped marine mammals, are, despite their northern circumpolar range, among the more unusual of the sound's rare visitors.

One of the most unexpected visitors to the North Shore arrived in August of 1995, when a manatee (Trichechus manatus) was spotted in the East River heading toward Long Island Sound. Manatees, also known as sea cows, are sea mammals seven to thirteen feet long and weighing up to thirteen hundred pounds. They live in the shallow brackish waters of lagoons and river mouths in the southeastern United States, primarily Florida. They are considered highly endangered, as their current population is only eighteen hundred animals. Adult manatees are vegetarians and have no enemies except man. Boat collisions with manatees account for most manatee deaths, and many surviving animals carry the propeller scars of such collisions. The manatee spotted in the East River had been named Chessie by a research scientist who, the previous October, had removed him from the cold waters of the Chesapeake Bay and returned him to his home along the east coast of Florida. For unknown reasons, Chessie had decided to make another unorthodox journey north and broke all known records for manatee travel. Chessie is a ten-foot-long-male weighing twelve hundred pounds and is between thirty and fifty years old. Unlike female manatees, it is not unusual

Large numbers of horseshoe crabs (*Limulus polyphemus*) crawl to the high water mark to lay their eggs in the sand during a new or full moon high tide in May.

for male manatees to wander outside their territory, but this was the first time a manatee ever wandered so far. One explanation might be the warmer than normal water temperatures recorded along the East Coast in the summer of 1995.

Marine turtles regularly visit the sound. The Kemp's ridley sea turtle (*Lepidochelys kempi*) is one of the rarest and most endangered marine reptiles in the world. Kemp's ridleys lay their eggs on a few beaches in Mexico, where their young hatch and then head out to sea, but little is known of their life cycle after this point. It appears, however, that a large number of adult Kemp's ridley turtles summer in Long Island Sound. We know this because in recent years there have been strandings of

Kemp's ridleys on beaches on eastern Long Island. Other marine turtles that occasionally summer in the sound includes the loggerhead turtle (*Caretta caretta*), the green turtle (*Chelonia mydas*), and the leatherback turtle (*Dermochelys coriacea*).

Shellfish are abundant in the protected harbors along Long Island's North Shore. The oyster (*Crassostrea virginica*) is one of the most important and celebrated of a long list of shellfish found within the sound's bays. At one time, there were expansive oyster beds along the shore, hence Oyster Bay. Oysters are large bivalve mollusks with a rough textured, variably shaped shell. They feed by extracting nutrients from water that they filter through their gills and a single oyster can filter as much as one hundred gallons of water per day. The palatability of oysters makes them prime candidates for predation. By the mid-nineteenth century oystering had become a huge industry on Long Island, and it continues today. Natural predators of oysters are too numerous to name and include other mollusks, sea stars, birds, marine worms, sponges, and crabs. A single female oyster may produce as many as one hundred million eggs a year; propagating countless young seems to be their most effective defense against extinction. Upon hatching, young oysters are quite unlike their parents and progress through several stages during development. They are first known as veligers and then trochophores that float at the water surface as members of the zooplankton community. The trochophores eventually develop into tiny oysters called "spat" that settle on some type of hard substrate, usually a pile of oyster shells, and grow into adults.

The oyster drill (Urosalpinx cinerea) is probably the most devastating natural predator of oysters. Like oysters, the oyster drill is a mollusk, but it has only one spiral-shaped shell. The oyster drill uses its radula, a small, rasplike part of the mouth, to drill a tiny round hole in the oyster shell and suck out its contents. Oyster drills regularly destroy 60 percent or more of local oyster seedbeds where spat grow. Oystermen who culture oysters avoid the drills by moving their oyster spat into areas with greater freshwater content tolerated by the oysters but not by the drills.

Sometimes, while walking along the beach, you may notice an oyster shell riddled with peculiar pockmarks, some so deep that they form small holes right through the shell. This is the work of boring sponges (Cliona spp.). Also known as sulfur sponges because of their yellow color and the sulfuric acid they secret to dissolve their host's shell, boring sponges are members of the phylum Porifera, the most primitive of all multicellular creatures. They are especially fond of oysters but

also attack other calcium-containing shelled marine life: by dissolving old shells they perform a valuable function, thereby cleaning the ocean floor and returning dissolved calcium to the water where growing shelled organisms can extract what they need.

The horseshoe crab (Limulus polyphemus), another denizen of the sound and other waters surrounding Long Island, must be considered one of the earth's most successful creatures, as it has survived unchanged since the Triassic Period (the first period of the dinosaurs 245 million years ago). Indeed, its earliest relatives date back to the Devonian period some 350 million years ago. The horseshoe crab is not a crab at all but instead belongs to the phylum Arthropoda, being more closely related to arachnids (like spiders, mites, and ticks) than to any species of crab. Its large, horseshoe-shaped, convex carapace, called the prosoma, triangular abdomen, and long spikelike tail combine to form an unforgettable image of aggression. Despite their menacing appearance, however, horseshoe crabs are by all accounts harmless creatures.

Horseshoe crabs roam shallow bay bottoms feeding on clams, worms, and other invertebrates, but in spring the crabs scramble ashore to lay their eggs. Beginning in mid-May along the North Shore's gently sloping, gravely beaches, or similar beaches anywhere else on Long Island, there occurs one of the most ancient breeding spectacles on Earth. When the tides are at their highest during a new or full moon, horseshoe crabs ascend the beaches to lay their eggs above the high-tide line. It sometimes looks as if hundreds of surf-rounded rocks had miraculously come to life to scurry about the beach in aimless abandon. The females, up to two feet long, are much larger than the males. The males attach themselves to the big females and the pair remains that way, sometimes for hours. It is not uncommon to see a large female lumbering about a beach with two or three little males attached. Eventually, she digs a burrow and lays two to three hundred small greenish eggs about one-eighth of an inch in diameter in it, and the male releas-

Overleaf:
A small tidal creek in Lloyd Harbor on the North Shore glows with delicate colors in the January twilight.

Laughing gulls (Larus atricilla) feeding on horseshoe-crab eggs.

Blue mussel shells *(Mytilus edulis)* and fallen petals of salt spray rose *(Rosa rugosa)* lie scattered along the beach at Target Rock National Wildlife Refuge on the Long Island Sound.

es his sperm to fertilize them. After several weeks of incubation, the sand-colored young hatch and enter the water, but stay close to shore as they begin to grow, moving eventually to deeper water and progressing through a series of exoskeleton molts until they become adults.

The heavily armored adult crabs have few enemies, but their eggs are the subject of a long chain of predation. The horseshoe crab's spring egg laying coincides with the arrival of migrating shorebirds from points south. Many shorebirds, including semi-palmated sandpipers *(Calidris pusilla)*, least sandpipers *(Calidris minutilla)*, ruddy turnstones *(Arenaria interpres)*, and black-bellied plovers *(Pluvialis dominica)*, have wintered in South America and must make the long, arduous trip to their breeding grounds in the Arctic each spring. They are voraciously hungry by the time they make landfall on Long Island, and the horseshoe crab eggs are a much needed, fattening delicacy easily exploited. To the south of Long Island on the Delaware Bay is the finest example of this phenomenon—almost 90 percent of the world's migraing red knots *(Calidris canutus)* gather to feast on the eggs. It is not uncommon to see sandpipers in the burrow with a female horseshoe crab, gobbling up her eggs as she deposits them; the ruddy turnstone's adeptness lies in locating and excavating the crab burrows for their treasured roe. Breeding pairs of Canada geese *(Branta canadensis)* bring their newly hatched goslings to feed on the eggs even though the adults, who are vegetarians, abstain. Mummichogs and other small fish devour eggs that end up loose in the surf. This activity attracts snowy egrets (*Egretta thula*) and great egrets (*Casmerodius albus*), who adeptly pluck the tiny fish from the water with their long, slender bills. When the horseshoe crabs mate, Long Island's beaches come alive, teaming with life until the tide recedes and all that remains are the few stranded crabs that were unable to make it back to the sanctuary of the surf.

Long Island's northern shoreline is quite different from its southern. There are no protective barrier islands or lagoons as on the South Shore, and so the sound has a profound and urgent effect on the silhouette of the island's northern border. The North Shore of western Long Island is a charming network of finely etched deep harbors not unlike the small coves and inlets of New England. Traveling east along the North Shore, however, the profile takes on a more homogeneous pattern. East of Mt. Sinai Harbor, the North Shore's protected coves give way to a smooth-edged facade buttressed by high cliffs clear to the tip of the North Fork.

Along the sound are some of Long Island's most scenic beaches. Absent are the monotony of the fine white sands found along the barrier islands. Instead, the sound has covered Long Island's North Shore beaches with a stunning variety of colorful, surf-rounded stones. Shells from blue mussels (*Mytilus edulis*) and slipper shells (*Crepidula fornicata*) augment the beaches' gemlike pebbles, sometimes in deep piles along the wrack line. Delicate shells are more often found intact along Long Island's northern beaches since, although formidable, the sound's surf is far less severe than that of the Atlantic Ocean. Particularly charming are the shells of the Atlantic jingle (*Anomia simplex*), a small bivalve clam that lives along the North Shore of Long Island. Like mussels, jingles have secret byssal threads (tough, protein fibers) that they use to anchor themselves to pebbles just below the low tide mark. They rely on the movements of the tides to bring them a constant supply of microscopic organisms and nutrients that they filter from the water. Jingle shells can be black, white, yellow, or orange and have a very shiny surface. They are delicate, thin, and translucent and when held up to the light look like tiny pieces of broken stained glass. Several of them tossed up and down in your hands make an audible jingle like wind chimes.

High, sheer cliffs flank many miles of Long Island's North Shore beaches, especially along its eastern end. Varying bands of gravel, sand, and clay sediments as well as numerous glacial boulders are their primary constituents. Some of the sediments are rich in iron and consequently possess a bright color that appears as distinct rusty colored bands in the sides of the cliffs. The clay sediments are usually a pasty gray hue. In some places the juxtapositions of the bands create striking patterns. Wave action from the sound undercuts the cliffs, causing them to crumble into the surf. Each year the sound pushes the sand and clay cliffs further south, with only their larger, heavier rocks remaining behind on the beaches.

The boulders and small stones scattered about the North Shore beaches are poignant reminders of how transient Long Island's shores are. The boulders, called erratics because they were carried to Long Island from the north by glaciers, represent a variety of minerals, including granites, gneiss, dolomite, and sandstone, making the North Shore beaches a veritable geologist's supermarket.

In several places, boulders of immense size stand as monolithic testaments to the powers of glaciers and erosion. One such spot is Target Rock National Wildlife Refuge in Lloyd Neck. Target rock is a huge piece of granite that lies just offshore and at low tide is almost completely exposed. Its name comes from the fact that during the American Revolution cannon crews on British warships used the rock for target practice.

The cliffs' layered sediments represent a timeline through our geological past. Younger sediments at the tops of the cliffs give way to progressively older depositions as you descend to shoreline. Some of the sediments are quite old, dating back to the Cretaceous period more than sixty-five million years ago. At Caumsett State Park in Lloyd Neck, an exposed Cretaceous sediment known as the Raritan Formation has yielded fossilized remains from those ancient times. Among the more interesting fossils are a number of large pieces of petrified wood. Fossil leaves from magnolia, eucalyptus, and fig trees provide evidence of a Cretaceous climate warmer than today's since, presently, similar plant communities thrive in much warmer regions than Long Island.

Long Island's North Shore cliffs yield other treasures besides fossils. Beachcombers walking below the cliffs sometimes find round balls of hardened clay and sand. These clay concretions are common in Long Island's Cretaceous deposits and come in various sizes, from tiny quarter-sized nuggets to large soccer ball-size globes. It is difficult to determine their age, but geologists agree that concretions can form rapidly and that most have appeared rela-

Overleaf:
Lloyd Harbor, seen here at low tide in winter, is typical of the fjordlike sheltered harbors along the North Shore of western Long Island.

tively recently. Concretions form when pockets of clay or clay-rich sands consolidate into a mass that serves as a nucleus for further lithification. The clay center allows for the precipitation of iron due to oxidation induced by pH changes as the concretion forms; consequently many concretions are rich in iron and have a characteristic rusty hue. Indian paint pots are special concretions that, when broken open, yield a hollow center filled with an ooze of iron-rich clay. As their name implies, Native Americans used Indian paint pots as a source of pigment.

The sheer cliffs of the North Shore serve as nesting habitats for a number of bird species. The belted kingfisher (Ceryle alcyon) is a crested bird, slate blue in color with short, stubby feet and a thick, oversized bill that appears much too large for a bird thirteen inches long. Kingfishers perch or sometimes hover, like tiny helicopters, over water, then plunge headfirst to catch a fish with their superbly adapted bills; they also use their bills and their stubby feet to excavate nesting burrows often several feet deep in soft banks along the cliffs, especially in areas close to rivers, streams, and ponds. Long Island's most noteworthy nesting cliff bird, however, is the bank swallow (Riparia riparia), a small, delicate, brown-backed bird with a grayish-brown band across its otherwise white breast. Like other members of the swallow family, bank swallows are capable of fantastic, high-speed aerial acrobatics while in pursuit of their insect diet. They nest along the sides of cliffs in deep burrows that they dig with their tiny beaks and feet—an amazing feat. Bank swallows are colonial birds and for years a colony of hundreds of them dotted the steep cliffs at Caumsett State Park with

their burrows, small, round holes about two inches in diameter. They were never present on Long Island in great numbers, but were locally common along several stretches of seaside cliffs. In recent years, however, their numbers have dwindled. The cause is a mystery.

Water birds nest sporadically along the North Shore. Common and least terns, piping plovers, willets, and oystercatchers are not as common as along the South Shore. One of the larger tern colonies is at the mouth of the Nissequogue River at Short Beach, where the offshore currents have formed fine-grained sand spits that the terns and the piping plovers seem to like.

The sandy shorelines favored by the terns and plovers attract an unexpected member of the plant community. Just back from the beach in open gravelly sands or sometimes hidden among the beach grass you can sometimes find a plant that might make you feel as if you are in a foreign landscape. Prickly pear (Opuntia compressa) is a succulent member of the cactus family that is locally common along the North Shore. Elsewhere on Long Island it is sporadic at best, but small colonies also exist on Fire Island and in Jamaica Bay, Queens. Prickly pear has fleshy rounded pads and spreads about three feet across and up to a foot high. It lacks the large spines found on many North American cacti but, instead, possesses short clusters of reddish-brown barbed bristles known as glochids. The glochids, often quite invisible, present a terrible nuisance for those unfortunate enough to have them lodged within their flesh.

Most people associate species of cactus with a desert environment. Deserts are defined as the driest of all terrestrial biomes and characterized by very low and

sporadic precipitation. Most of us assume that means a very hot climate, but there are deserts that exist in environments where the yearly average temperature is quite low. Therefore, it is not unusual to imagine cactus on Long Island because no matter how much rain falls on the beach the water quickly leaches through the porous sands, resulting in a de facto desert. The constant sea breeze also has a desiccating effect on vegetation, but prickly pears, like all cacti, have a number of adaptations that let them thrive in dry conditions. To curtail water loss, adaptive forces have reduced the prickly pear's leaves to spines, while the stems are thick and waxy, allowing for the storage and retention of water. Prickly pear extends along the coast as far north as Cape Cod and south to Florida in the appropriate habitats. In mid-June, the prickly pear produces beautiful large (up to four inches across), lemon yellow flowers. These fade quickly, and before long, pear-shaped, reddish fruits adorn the succulent pads. The fruits are edible, as are the pads, and Native Americans used them in their diet, being ever so careful to avoid the glochids. Wildlife makes use of the prickly pear as well. Box turtles (Terrapene carolina) will make a meal of the prickly pear at any time, being equally fond of the flowers, fruits, and pads.

Many species of the aforementioned flora and fauna make their homes elsewhere on Long Island and other points along the East Coast of the United States. However, the Long Island Sound and Long Island's North Shore together comprise a number of important habitats whose diversity of life and range of aesthetic beauty are rarely matched by other eastern seaboard shorelines.

Beaches along the North Shore, such as this one near the mouth of the Nissequogue River, are typically made up of pebbles and small stones, unlike the white sand beaches of the South Shore's barrier islands.

Glacial erratics capped with ice
lie below the bluffs at Caumsett
State Park. Erosion by wave
action from the Long Island
Sound is slowly undercutting the
cliffs. Occasionally large boulders
within the gravelly bluffs drop to
the beach, and are too heavy
for the littoral currents to carry
them away.

Opposite:
High bluffs of sand, gravel, and
clay are characteristic of the
North Shore coastline. Pictured
here are the clay-rich bluffs at
the David Weld Sanctuary in the
village of Nissequogue.

Prickly pear (*Opuntia compressa*), seen here at East Beach on Huntington Bay, is the only cactus native to Long Island. In June, its showy blossoms bring color to the dry sandy soils of the North Shore's beaches.

Target Rock at Target Rock National Wildlife Refuge in Lloyd Neck is reputed to have been used for target practice by Colonial naval vessels. The Connecticut shoreline is visible across the Long Island Sound.

CHAPTER 5

THE HARDWOOD FORESTS
AND THE HEMPSTEAD PLAINS

Across northern Long Island, the processes of glaciation left a land of
rolling hills and fertile soil. Upland forests of deciduous hardwoods, rivaling
in magnificence the great woodlands of the Appalachians, covered the land
until the arrival of European settlers. (Deciduous trees, which lose their
leaves in the autumn, tend to have harder wood than coniferous ever-
greens such as pine and cedar; hence the name "hardwoods.") More than
seventy species of trees shadowed the forest floor right up to the North
Shore's pebbly beaches. The dense canopy was occasionally broken by the
numerous kettle ponds that filled the deep depressions between undulating
hills. American chestnut *(Castanea dentata)* and various species of hicko-
ries and oaks dominated much of the better-drained areas. Great groves of
tulip trees *(Liriodendron tulipifera)*, reaching heights of 150 feet, occupied
the forest's wetter margins.

The arrival of European settlers would forever change the character of the island's indigenous forests. The demand for wood to build homesteads and farms caused the first depredations. Soon, the island's forests were supplying cordwood for fuel to an expanding New York City, while a growing merchant marine and whaling industry took great numbers of white oak (Quercus alba) to satisfy the need for tall ship masts. After more than three hundred years of settlement, a few hundred acres on Gardiner's Island is all that remains today of Long Island's primary growth hardwood forests. All the rest is second growth.

From Europe and Asia came plagues such as Dutch elm disease and chestnut blight. Chestnut blight, caused by an introduced fungus, set out on its destructive path in New York City in 1904. Within forty years it eliminated the American chestnut as one of the dominant hardwoods of the eastern United States. Chestnut blight girdles young trees by attacking the cambium (that is, the growth layer) beneath the bark. With devastating ferocity the blight diminished the once mighty chestnut forests to little more than bushy sprouts growing from the roots of ancient trees. Most reach a height of no more than twenty feet before they succumb. A walk through Long Island's upland forests will undoubtedly take you past a number of struggling chestnut sprouts, pathetic reminders of their species' past glory.

The greatest change, however, came in the mid-twentieth century when suburban sprawl radiating out from New York City consumed the forests at an alarming rate. Today, little remains of the island's once extensive green canopy. Only small stands of woods in parks and along the not-so-densely developed North Shore give us an idea of what Long Island's upland forests were once like. Hardwood forests traditionally occupied a broad band that extended along the northern portion of the island from Queens eastward, roughly shadowing the Harbor Hill Moraine, into the North Fork. In central Long Island, in what is now Nassau County, the hardwood forests unexpectedly give way to a vast prairie of grasses with few if any trees. These Hempstead Plains formed a break in the hardwoods to the north, west, and south, and the softwood species of the pine barrens to the east. Upland forests also can be found along the crest of the Ronkonkoma Moraine, extending into the South Fork. Deciduous woodlands grow along portions of the South Shore, although they differ in species composition from the upland forests to the north. Small pockets of hardwoods also thrive scattered throughout the island where the geology dictates habitat hospitable to their growth. Oak and hickory dominated forests grow wherever the ground is fertile and not too wet. In wet areas near streams, kettle ponds, and swamps, these species give way to moisture-loving tulip, tupelo, and red maple, while chestnut oak and mountain laurel dominate the drier ridge tops.

A variety of animals from large to small inhabit the upland forests. Larger mammals such as beaver (Castor canadensis), gray wolf (Canis lupus), black bear (Ursus americanus), and bobcat (Lynx rufus) once roamed the woods, but they vanished long ago. Today, even deer are absent from most of the North Shore's forests, having been driven into the pine barrens and other unoccupied areas. Nevertheless, a rich fauna still occurs in undisturbed areas. Not surprisingly, raccoons (Procyon lotor) and opossums (Didelphis marsupialis) thrive in these enclaves. Their numbers are probably greater today than historically because they have learned to thrive off the waste of human settlements. At night they make their raids on garbage cans and road kills, returning to the refuge of the woods during daylight. Red fox (Vulpes fulva) are plentiful wherever there is growth to supply enough cover to hide a den. They, too, have learned to live successfully in the shadow of suburbia. Gray squirrels (Sciurus carolinensis) and chipmunks (Tamias striatus) scurry among the flowers on the forest floor. Woodchucks (Marmota monax) have been steadily declining, especially since the open agricultural areas they prefer gave way to housing developments. As late as the early 1980s, they survived in Nassau County along Northern State Parkway, but the pressures of development have pushed them further east. Skunks (Mephitis mephitis), which were once plentiful, have not fared very well either. The last time I personally saw a skunk on Long Island was in Cold Spring Harbor in the early 1970s. The absence of skunks is curious because, like raccoons, they usually adapt well to settled areas.

You are unlikely to meet a skunk in the upland forests, but you may come across their primary predator, the great horned owl (Bubo virginianus). These large birds (around two feet in length) possess two distinguishing ear tufts that, in the darkness of night, resemble horns. They remain locally common along the North Shore and in the pine barrens as well; their preference for mature

Sweetgum fruit litters the forest floor. The round balls are composed of many sharply pointed woody capsules, giving the fruit a spiny texture.

Right:
Golden waxy cap mushrooms (*Hygrophorus flavescens*) emerge from the leaf litter of an oak-dominated woodland in Forest Park, Queens.

forests and their nocturnal habits, however, make them difficult to find. Their breeding cycle begins as early as January, before most other birds', and is marked by an increase in their distinctive hooting cry as males attract mates and establish territories. Great horned owls are superbly suited to their role of Long Island's largest winged nocturnal predator. Their vision is equally acute in daylight and darkness, and they possess large talons to impale their prey, which ranges from mice to squirrels and everything in between, as they swiftly descend from the night sky. Their hearing is so effective that they rely on it as much as vision when hunting. The facial feathers of the great horned owl form a parabolic receptor called a facial disc that captures and directs sound to their ears. Because the ear opening on one side of the head is larger than the opening on the other, the owl can triangulate on sounds to locate its prey in the dark. As if this isn't enough of an advantage, the owl's flight feathers are serrated and act to dampen its wing noise, improving its ability to hear sounds from below over the noise of its own flight.

Admittedly, the great horned owl is not a bird that most Long Islanders will come across often, but there are hundreds of other avian species to observe. During spring and summer, the forests ring with the song of birds that come to raise their young or those that briefly stop by on their way to points north. A number of interesting migratory songbirds inhabit the second-growth upland woodlands along the North Shore. Male, blue-winged warblers *(Vermivora pinus)* are attractive summer residents, with a bright yellow head and breast and bluish-gray wings

with two white wing bars. Evolution has dealt the female a duller version of the male's handsome plumage. Blue-winged warblers seem to prefer the areas where forest and clearings meet. One good place to see them is the Muttontown Nature Preserve in Nassau County. In early summer it seems that almost all the larger trees have a resident red-eyed vireo *(Vireo olivaceus)*. These are small, rather drab green songbirds with a peculiar red eye. What they lack in looks, they make up for with a vociferous song repeated without interruption for the better part of the day. They are one of the most common birds in the woodlands of the eastern United States, but when summer departs so too do the vireos, migrating south to warmer, winter headquarters. The American robin *(Turdus migratorius)* is one of the most familiar migratory songbirds that breeds on Long Island. Handsome members of the thrush family, robins frequent upland forests (and suburban lawns), where they methodically search for earthworms. The wood thrush *(Hylocichla mustelina)* prefers deciduous forests, where its loud, liquid song is one of the most distinctive sounds of twilight during the breeding season. Again, Muttontown Nature Preserve is the best place to see and hear them, although occasionally the birds can be found nesting among suburban homes where the trees are mature and the understory dense. Another upland forest bird that breeds at Muttontown is the wood pewee *(Contopus borealis)*, a nondescript member of the flycatcher family *(Tyrannidae spp.)* that spends the day hawking insects from the sky. Wood pewees usually stay high in the trees, and if it were not for their plaintive call, a slow whistled "pee-a-wee," they would go unnoticed.

Raccoons *(Procyon lotor)* exploit the most densely populated suburban areas by using storm drains for shelter and dens.

Overleaf:
A dense stand of sweetgum *(Liquidambar styraciflua)* is enshrouded in morning fog in a wooded margin in southern Nassau County.

Long Island's deciduous
woodlands in autumn.

Sweetgums in winter. Sweetgum is a common tree of the coastal plain and is characteristically found in the narrow band of hardwoods along Long Island's South Shore.

The American woodcock
(Scolopax minor) is an odd-looking member of the shorebird family that breeds in open, moist fields, where it uses its long sensitive bill to probe the ground for earthworms. During spring evenings males perform an elaborate aerial courtship display.

In contrast to summering song-birds are the woodland birds that use Long Island as a winter retreat from their summering grounds to the north. The yellow-bellied sap-sucker *(Sphyrapicus varius)* is a species of woodpecker whose unusual feeding habits account for its entertaining name. Sapsuckers will drill orderly rows of holes in suitable trees and extract sap. Their primary intent, however, is to leave the scene and allow sap to ooze for a while. Eventually sugars in the sap will attract insects that the sapsuckers happily eat upon return to their drillings. The fox sparrow *(Passerella iliaca)* is another northern breeding bird that winters in small numbers on Long Island. Fox sparrows are much larger than most other spar-rows and have a reddish color like the pelt of a fox. They usually arrive on the island sometime in November and associate with other species of birds in winter foraging groups, often making appearances at suburban bird feeders. The dark-eyed junco *(Junco hyemalis)* is another mem-ber of the sparrow family that uses Long Island as a winter retreat. Juncos appear suddenly in autumn, often in great numbers, and remain conspicuous residents throughout the winter. They spend most of their time foraging on the ground, where their slate gray wings and bodies contrast sharply with winter snow. Most wintering songbirds forego the verbalization of their characteristic songs, either remaining silent or uttering no more than alarm notes and erratic chatter. The white-throated sparrow *(Zonotrichia albicollis)* is one winter resident that favors the forest with its flutelike five-note song during even the gloomiest of winter days. It is an attractive bird with a white-and-black striped crown and, of course, a bold white patch on its throat.

There are also year-round avian residents in the upland forests. The spectacular red-bellied wood-pecker *(Melanerpes carolinus)* is a decidedly southern species and Long Island is approximately at the northern limit of its range. The belly of the bird actually offers nothing more than an inconspicu-ous blush of color; the male of the species, however, possesses a rich scarlet crown and nape and is not easily overlooked. The birds also have a striking black-and-white barred pattern across their backs. Noisy birds that make their pres-ence known with a loud, nasal cry, red-bellied woodpeckers are espe-cially fond of mature hardwoods along the island's northern ridge. Forest Park, Queens, is one of the surest places to see them. In recent years they can occasionally be encountered along the South Shore as well. Another year-round resident that favors the same habitat as the red-bellied wood-pecker is the tufted titmouse *(Parus bicolor).* This small (about six and a half inches in length) gray, white-breasted bird has crown feathers that form a small crest on top of its head and a ring-ing three-note call. They travel in little bands and even in the winter their noisy chatter brings warmth to the forest. The tufted titmouse is another southern species that is close to the northern limit of its range on Long Island and is a recent arrival on Long Island, as well: it was not until the 1960s that they began to breed here regularly. The closely related black-capped chickadee *(Parus atricapillus),* Long Island's smallest year-round bird, is about an inch shorter than the tufted titmouse. Like the tit-mice, chickadees travel in merry little bands in search of food except during the breeding sea-son, when their priorities rest elsewhere.

Where forests were once cleared for farmland, there are bound to be fields and meadows. At Caumsett State Park there are good breeding populations of ring-necked pheasant *(Phasianus colchicus)*, a nonnative from Asia originally stocked here as a game bird that survives today because the fields remain. The cryptically colored female tends the nest that it builds on the ground. In contrast, the handsomely decorated male has iridescent green head feathers, a white collar, and fleshy red eye patches. The male makes a disturbing territorial call that sounds as if he's hacking up his lungs. The bobwhite *(Colinus virginianus)*, another common game bird of the fields, has a pleasant whistled call that sounds like its name: "bob-white."

Other field-nesting birds include field sparrows *(Spizella pusilla)*, eastern meadowlark *(Sturnella magna)*, American goldfinch *(Carduelis tristis)*, and indigo bunting *(Passerina cyanea)*. Chipping sparrows *(Spizella passerina)* were at one time the common sparrow of gardens and yards on Long Island, but became rare through competition with introduced species such as the house sparrow *(Passer domesticus)*. In the open grounds of Caumsett, they still remain in good numbers and during summer their trill-like song is a familiar sound.

Muttontown Nature Preserve also has open fields and if you visit in April, you may hear in early evening a curious nasal noise sounding like "peent" emanating from the fields. This is the mating call of the American woodcock *(Scolopax minor)*, an eleven-inch shorebird with a peculiar appearance: it has short stubby legs, a large flat-topped head with eyes set well to the rear, and a long sen-

sitive bill used to probe for earthworms. During spring evenings, males engage in an elaborate courting display where they rise high in the sky and then drop back to earth in a zigzag fashion. Air forced through their feathers during this ritual produces this eerie whistling sound.

While birds cheer the treetops, wildflowers add their special charm to the forest floor. Like stars in the evening sky, a multitude of wildflowers brightens the upland forests each spring. Canada May flowers *(Maianthemuym canadense)* are tiny wildflowers that, as their name suggests, bloom in May and carpet the forest floor with a mat of tiny white flowers on top of dainty stalks. They have small heart-shaped leaves that are deep green in color, reflecting the forest's canopy above. By early fall, small red berries appear on the flower stalks. Another wildflower that blooms in early May is the wood anemone *(Anemone quinquefolia)*, which grows in mats no more than eight inches high. Each plant bears a single-stalked white flower above a whorl of deeply cut leaves that have a delicate lacelike quality. The plant has no petals, and its flowers are actually made up of five white sepals that take the place of petals to attract pollinators. Sepals are modified leaves, usually green, whose normal function is to enclose and protect flower buds before they open. Unlike the Canada May flowers, which thrive throughout the forest, wood anemones grow sporadically across the island in rich open woodlands, where they favor somewhat sunny spots. Windflower is another name for these beauties because their delicately stalked flowers tremble and sway in even the slightest draft. At times a mat of wood anemones kinetically shaking in the breeze

Bobwhites *(Colinus virginianus)* are particularly common in the large meadows at Caumsett State Park in Lloyd Neck.

appears poised to lift up from the ground and move away. Yellow trout lily *(Erythronium americanum)* is yet another early spring bloomer, often showing off its lovely yellow flowers before the trees present their leaves. Later in summer, wood geraniums *(Geranium maculatum)*, with their pale lavender flowers, brighten the dark corners of the forest.

Less common than these are the trilliums. There are three species of trillium found on the island: purple trillium *(Trillium erectum)*, painted trillium *(Trillium undulatum)*, and nodding trillium *(Trillium cernuum)*. All three have leaves and flowers arranged in threes or multiple of threes, hence the name *tri*llium. Trilliums prefer moist oak woodlands where they bloom in April and May. Purple trilliums—the most common of the three and rare at that—grow about a foot tall and have a single reddish-purple flower with an unpleasant odor (their common name is stinking Benjamin). The foul smell serves not only to keep away flower pickers but to attract

Overleaf:
Canada May flowers *(Maianthemuym canadense)* in bloom on the forest floor of a white oak *(Quercus alba)* dominated woodland in Muttontown Nature Preserve.

Despite their size, mourning cloaks *(Nymphalis antiopa)* are difficult to see on account of their cryptic coloration: their brown, jagged edged, folded wings bear a remarkable resemblance to dead leaves. If a butterfly positions itself the right way it will blend imperceptibly with the forest. This pair is mating.

The Appalachian brown *(Satyrodes appalachia)* is an uncommon butterfly on Long Island. Its muted earthy tones are a perfect compliment to the wooded areas it inhabits. It prefers wooded margins near wet areas.

carrion flies as pollinators. The other two species of trillium lack the purple trillium's unpleasant odor but match and even surpass the beauty of its flower. Nodding trillium has a drooping white flower with recurved petals, and painted trillium has a white flower highlighted with red veining that intensifies and becomes a red band in the flower's center.

The sweet nectars of Long Island's woodland wildflowers attract a variety of woodland butterflies species. The mourning cloak *(Nymphalis antiopa)* is probably the first butterfly to appear in spring. It overwinters as an adult, while most other butterfly species pass the winter through the egg, larval, or pupal stage. On warm, sunny winter days it occasionally emerges from its protective hideaway and takes flight for the day, often while snow is still on the ground. This large butterfly (up to three inches across) is one of the most exquisitely colored on Long

Island: both upper and lower wings have a deep velvety maroon color, evoking the plush robes of ancient royalty. A row of tiny sky blue dots decorates the wing's outer margin, followed by a brilliant creamy yellow terminal band. When at rest, the wings are folded to reveal the understated earth tones of the wings' undersurface, colors that provide superb camouflage in a woodland habitat. If you startle a resting mourning cloak while walking through the woods, it will spring into the air with an audible click of its wings and a flash of color designed to thwart predators. The large wood nymph *(Cercyonis pegala)* is another common butterfly of Long Island's deciduous woodlands. Like the mourning cloak, wood nymphs are cryptically colored and they also overwinter as adults. They have large eyespots on the upper wing that lie in a yellowish orange band that contrasts distinctly with their overall chocolate brown color. Wood-nymph larva feed on various species of grasses; consequently they frequent the sunny margins of wooded areas where grasses grow. Stillwell Woods Preserve in Nassau County has good numbers of wood nymphs during the early summer. The spring azure *(Celastrina ladon)* is another butterfly that makes an early appearance in Long Island's deciduous woodlands, scurrying about erratically no more than a few feet from the ground. Appearing during the first warm days of April, spring azures are quite small, no more than the size of a quarter, and their folded wings are silver with small dark marks while their open wings reveal an overall deep blue color. They are a multibrooded species, meaning that several life cycles from egg to adult occur during any given year. Curiously, the different broods exhibit variation in color and markings from each other.

Many multibrooded butterfly species exhibit this phenomenon.

Butterflies are members of the insect order, *Lepidoptera,* which also includes the moths. The difference between moths and butterflies is sometimes quite obvious, but on occasion the characteristics that we generally use to distinguish the two are nebulous. Most people know the butterflies as diurnal creatures while moths are familiar to us as nocturnal insects. Furthermore, butterflies have clublike ends to their antennae while moths' antennae lack this or are feathery. Moths tend to rest with their wings folded flat, while butterflies rest with their wings folded upright. These characteristic descriptions have many exceptions. For example, on Long Island there are a number of moths that are exclusively diurnal. The bumblebee moth (*Hemaris thysbe*) is a day-flying member of the sphinx (*Sphingidae*) moth family. Bumblebee moths are about one and a quarter inches across with fat yellow-and-black bodies and relatively clear wings that beat extremely rapidly. They hover about flowers during the day, extracting nectar with their long proboscises and, in doing so, remarkably resemble bumblebees engaged in similar activity. Most other members of the sphinx family feed similarly, but do so nocturnally. Another diurnal moth common on Long Island is the ctenuchid moth (*Ctenucha virginica*). Ctenuchid moths are small (about one and a half inches across), with brown wings, a metallic blueish-green body, orange head, and feathery antennae. They are quite common in late summer and are often found nectaring on late summer blooming wildflowers such as goldenrod (*Solidago*) and asters.

The cecropia moth (*Hyalophora cecropia*) is the largest nocturnal moth on Long Island, with a wingspan reaching almost six inches. Cecropia moths have brownish wings with rusty-red shading throughout; each wing has a white-and-red crossband and a white crescent-shaped mark. At the tip of the forewing is a small light-purple region with an eyespot marking. Cecropia larva feed on a variety of host plants, including dogwood, birch, wild cherry, willow, and maple. The caterpillars, when ready to pupate in the fall, are huge, up to four and a half inches long and as thick as an adult man's thumb. They overwinter as pupas in large brownish cocoons. In May, the cocoon completes metamorphosis and an adult emerges. Unlike the sphinx moth, cecropia moths do not feed. They live for only a week or two with the one purpose of finding a mate and breeding to perpetuate the next year's generation. It is noteworthy that the majority of the life span of any individual generation of cecropia moth occurs entombed in a cocoon where it undergoes a complete restructuring of its internal organs and external appearance.

Finally, we cannot leave the forest proper without mentioning red-backed salamanders (*Plethedon cinereus*). These terrestrial salamanders lay their eggs in moist microenvironments under logs or stones. Since they do not depend on ponds for breeding, as Long Island's mole salamanders do (see below), they have been able to colonize much greater areas. Scientists estimate that red-backed salamanders make up more of the biomass in eastern forests than any other vertebrate. As someone who has spent many years in the field on Long Island, I find this difficult to believe: these creatures are, indeed, easy to find,

Polyphemus moths (*Antheraea polyphemus*) nearly rival the cecropia in size; they are also nocturnal and have a similar life cycle, although they usually fly a little later in the summer than cecropias. The moth is named after the mythological Greek one-eyed giant Polyphemus because of the large, colorful eyespots on its hind wing. These striking markings help ward off would-be predators because they resemble the eyes of a large predator, such as an owl.

but do not appear to me to be present in the numbers necessary to support this claim. Red-backed salamanders are long (two to five inches) and slender. They have a dark dorsal side with a bold brick-red dorsal stripe extending from head to tail; on the ventral side, they are light with small dark spots. Red-backed salamanders occur in two color morphs: the red-backed is typical, but some individuals, called "lead back," are totally gray and lack the red stripe. Normally the two morphs intermingle, but on Long Island their populations appear divided, with the typical form living among the upland forests of the North Shore while the lead backs dominate the pine barrens.

Red-backed salamanders
(Plethodon cinereus) are common woodland inhabitants throughout Long Island.

Along the dry ridges of the moraine the forest composition changes. The white oaks give way to chestnut oaks *(Quercus prinus)*, and the understory is dominated by mountain laurel *(Kalima latifolia)*, an attractive evergreen shrub of the heath family, with white to pinkish clustered flowers. In June, the laurel groves burst into bloom in a display unrivaled by the most magnificent cultivated gardens. Nassau County, most notably Stillwell Woods Preserve, has some of the finest laurel groves on the island.

The whorled pogonia *(Isotria verticillata)*, with one or two small greenish-yellow flowers above a whorl of five leaves, is a small orchid that is locally common in this habitat. The small whorled pogonia *(Isotria medeoloides)* is a smaller relative of the whorled pogonia with an unusual characteristic. Subsequent to blooming, the plant will enter a rest period where it lies dormant for at least ten years before blooming again. Consequently, it is difficult to find and is among the rarest plants in North America. Historically, it has occurred on Long Island.

Pink lady's slippers *(Cypripedium acaule)* are orchids that prefer dry soil and therefore are right at home in the deciduous forests along the island's glacial moraines. Mature plants have two large green-ribbed, basal leaves; sometime in May they produce a leafless flower stalk about a foot high with, usually, a single flower that many describe as resembling pink footwear, hence the name lady's slipper or moccasin flower. I think they look more like tiny, drooping, alien cerebrums complete with a longitudinal fisure and a weblike network of blood-red veins. However they are described, these are strikingly beautiful plants possessing an exotic quality unusual to Long Island's flora. Attempts to transplant lady's slipper orchids often result in failure, as the plant exists in a delicate mutualistic relationship with a mycorrhizal fungus bound to its root system that helps supply it with nutrients, and disturbance usually disrupts this relationship, resulting in the orchid's death. It is best to admire them but not dig them up.

Throughout Long Island, there are small, round pools of water called kettle ponds. These look like they are the water-filled impressions left by giant kettles, and the reader will not be surprised to learn that they are further artifacts of the ice ages. During the last period of glaciation, the great weight of massive continental ice sheets compressed the ground. As the climate warmed and melting began, the ground, relieved of the ice's tremendous weight, sprung back rapidly but unevenly. The lower depressions collected and held water, becoming kettle ponds. Kettle ponds also formed when a piece of ice from a retreating glacier broke off and became lodged in the ground. As the glacier continued its retreat, till and sediments suspended in its meltwater rushed over and around the dislodged piece of ice, often burying it. In due time, the ice melted, the sediments above it collapsed into the void, and a round depression was left. Some kettles are so-called water-table ponds; these very deep depressions intersect the upper limits of glacial aquifers and have a constant water supply. (Glacial aquifers are stores of subterranean water trapped in layers of sediments.) Lake Ronkonkoma in Suffolk County is such a kettle, and also the island's largest and deepest body of water, covering 243 acres with a maximum depth of ninety-seven feet. In contrast, perched kettle ponds are shallow and lie above the water table in impermeable clay-rich soils. Rain is the primary water source for these kettles, and their water level fluctuates according to the seasonal rainfalls that occur from autumn to spring. Vernal pools are shallow kettles that dry out each year by midsummer.

Within the North Shore's woodlands, most kettle ponds are small and of the vernal variety. During the spring when the water table is high from spring rains and winter thaw, these ponds fill. In the heat of summer, the water table falls and the vernal pools dry up. The transitory character of vernal pools provides a unique environment for several species of flora and fauna. Obviously, fish cannot survive in vernal pools. Various species of amphibians take advantage of this by laying their eggs almost exclusively in vernal pools. In this way, young amphibian larva, which are gilled, water-breathing creatures, can develop in an environment relatively safe from aquatic predation. This strategy seems to work just fine, except

when a ravenous water bird devastates a vernal pool's young amphibian population. Muttontown Nature Preserve has a particularly good example of a vernal pool habitat. One year, I watched a green-backed heron (Butorides striatus) over a period of two weeks as it methodically removed anything that moved in one particular vernal pool there. Green-backed herons have long legs for wading in water and a spearlike bill attached to a whip-action neck. They sometimes stalk but more often sit and wait at the water's edge until the appropriate prey crosses their path; then they lash out with lightning speed to capture their meal.

The North Shore's vernal ponds host a parade of breeding amphibians from March to June. One of the first is the spotted salamander (Ambystoma laterale), a member of the mole family of salamanders, so named because they remain buried beneath the ground for most of the year, only appearing on the surface briefly to breed. Spotted salamanders are handsome jet black animals, six to eight inches long, with yellow or orange spots arranged in an irregular row along each side of the back. They possess skin glands that give them an unpalatable taste and predators recognize their conspicuous markings as a signal of the salamander's foul taste; a species whose markings serve to warn predators is said to possess aposematic coloration. Spotted salamanders arrive, sometimes in large numbers, to vernal ponds after the earliest spring rains. There, the salamanders participate in a curious behavior resembling frenzied dirty dancing, as the males thrash around, whipping their tails from side to side, while the females become intertwined. Scientists once believed that the males' actual movements specifi-

cally served to attract females, but it is now known that the females respond to a chemical released by the males. The elaborate tail thrashing serves to disperse the chemical messengers precisely so that the females can follow a concentration gradient of molecules to the male. The salamanders lay a round orange-sized mass containing hundreds of eggs encased in a protective gelatinous protein. Within several weeks the gilled larvae, which resemble frog tadpoles, hatch, and they remain in the vernal pool until metamorphosing into the adult form some months later.

As a young boy I can remember hiking by a small vernal pond early one April and hearing a quack from the water without a sign of waterfowl about. This puzzled me for some time, until much later I learned that wood frogs (Rana sylvatica) skulking about the pond produced the curious noise. The vocalizations of wood frogs faithfully mimic the quacking of a duck. Around the same time that spotted salamanders reach the ponds, wood frogs make their appearance, and their voices can often be heard around ponds before all the surface ice has melted. While spotted salamanders may go unnoticed, the cacophonous presence of wood frogs is easily detectable during the spring breeding season. They breed with haste, sometimes attracting a mate, laying eggs, and exiting the vernal pools in a few days time. This is unlike other frogs that may linger in the breeding pools for weeks following egg laying. Apart from their breeding season, wood frogs hide among leaf litter on the forest floor, appearing occasionally on damp days searching for their varied insect prey.

Male spring peepers (*Hyla crucifer*) have a loud, piercing call with a bell-like quality that is produced by a large inflatable vocal sac under their chins. In attracting a mate, they usually utter high-pitched whistles in intervals of about one second, but the rate can be faster or slower depending on ambient air temperature. They occasionally emit a trill-like call with the same piercing fervor.

Opposite:
Duckweed (*Lemnaceae spp.*), a tiny aquatic plant, floats in whirled patterns on the surface of a vernal kettle pond in Muttontown Nature Preserve.

Page 92:
Pink lady's slipper (*Cypripedium acaule*) blossoms peak through the fronds of hay-scented fern (*Dennstaedtia punctilobula*). Lady's slippers are showy orchids that bloom in early summer and are common on Long Island, occasionally occurring in large stands.

Page 93:
Skunk cabbage (*Symplocarpus foetidus*) emerges through a March snow at Shu Swamp.

Spring peepers (*Hyla crucifer*) arrive at the ponds a little after the wood frogs. During the evening, groups of peepers sing loud choruses that can be deafening upon close approach, only to end abruptly in silence once the intruder reaches a critical distance to the breeding pool. Spring peepers vary from brown to olive to gray with a dark mark in the shape of a cross on their backs; at approximately one inch long, they are Long Island's smallest tree frog. Arboreal in habit, they make their home among the woodland's shrubs and trees, where they feed on insects. (Interestingly, all of the world's adult amphibians are carnivores, most feeding on insects, while most amphibian larva have herbivorous diets, feeding on algae.) Tree frogs have evolved curious adaptations that allow them to live above the ground. They have long limbs for climbing and, at the terminus of each toe, they have an adhesive disk that allows them to cling efficiently to vegetation.

Later in the summer the island's only other tree frog, the gray tree frog, makes its breeding appearance at the local kettle pond. Gray tree frogs are larger than peepers (about one and a half to two inches long) with a warty-skinned back resembling a toad more than a tree frog. Their color is usually gray or greenish, but many intermediates and variations occur. They spend their time foraging in small trees and shrubs often close to wetlands and ponds. Like so many of Long Island's amphibians, the gray tree frog goes unnoticed most of the year except during the June mating season when the males gather at small ponds and call to attract a mate. Two superficially identical species, *Hyla versicolor* and *Hyla chrysoscelis,* go by the common name gray tree frogs. They have overlapping ranges, but their trill-like calls differ somewhat, and when the two species are singing together, *versicolor* may be distinguished by its slower cadence. Genetically, *versicolor* is tetraploid, meaning that it contains twice as many chromosomes as its diploid relative, *chrysoscelis.*

Other summer breeding frogs include green frogs (*Rana clamitans melanota*) and bullfrogs (*Rana catsbeiana*), but unlike the amphibians that use kettle ponds only during the breeding period, these two species live permanently in and around water. Like so many other amphibians, the green frog is variable in color, ranging from green to brown and everything in-between. They have two dorsolateral ridges on their backs that help distinguish them from the similar bullfrog, whose back is smooth. During the June breeding period they utter their distinctive call, which sounds like a pinging twang often described as a plucked banjo string. Bullfrogs are the largest frogs on Long Island, with bodies about six inches long. Like the green frogs, they are vocal summer breeders, with a jug-o'-rum call that is loud and toward the low end of the musical scale. Breeding males have enlarged forearms and thumbs, an adaptation that helps them during amplexus. Amplexus is when the male grabs the female in the pectoral or pelvic region. A pair may remain in amplexus for days until the female is ready to release her eggs, at which time the male assists by gently squeezing her sides. Fertilization is external, completed when the male releases sperm as the eggs are being laid.

The flora around kettle ponds, streams, and swamps consists of moisture-loving species not otherwise found in the upland forest. Buttonbush (*Cephalanthus occidentalis L.*) is an aquatic shrub

that is right at home growing with its roots in the water. It has small creamy white flowers arranged in ball-like clusters and when in bloom during the early summer is an attractive host to nectaring bees and butterflies. Just back from the waterline grows spicebush *(Lindera benzoin),* a somewhat larger shrub, reaching a height of twelve feet. In early spring, before any leaves have appeared, its small yellow flowers brighten the landscape. The leaves and twigs and reddish berries are aromatic when crushed and have been used for teas as well as food flavoring. The twigs and berries are also an important food source for many animals, ranging from deer to rabbits and birds. The spicebush swallowtail *(Papilio troilus)* is a butterfly whose larva feed on spicebush. Swallowtails are members of the family *Papilionidae,* whose representatives on Long Island include tiger swallowtails *(Papilio glaucus),* black swallowtails *(Papilio polyxenes),* and occasionally pipevine swallowtails *(Papilio philenor).* They are all fairly large butterflies, and each has narrow, tail-like projections on its hind wings, hence the name swallowtail. Spicebush swallowtails are about four to five inches across and are mostly black, with the males having a greenish sheen on the inside hind wing; in females this is often bluish. The spicebush swallowtail is common in shaded woods on Long Island, and the territorial males can often be seen aggressively patrolling a wooded glade where they swoop intruders, including people.

The wet margins around ponds, streams, and swamps are home to a number of beautiful wildflowers. Marsh marigolds *(Caltha palustris)* often grow right in the water in bushy tufts, and in early spring

provide a dazzling spatter of color to the woodlands. Their colorful blooms do not look much at all like garden marigolds, resembling buttercups more than anything else. Like the wood anemone, the marsh marigold is unusual in that its petals are absent and its flowers result from golden-yellow sepals in place of petals. Another wildflower that likes to have its roots in the water is the blue flag *(Iris versicolor).* With its narrow swordlike leaves and flowers with violet-blue petals that appear cupped by three blue veined sepals with a yellow base, they very much resemble the cultivated iris species available at nurseries across the island. The yellow flag *(Iris pseudacorus)* is a European plant that has escaped from cultivation and established itself in the wild, now competing for the same niche as our native blue flag. Its flowers are a little smaller than the blue flag's, which can be up to four inches across, and are completely yellow.

Skunk cabbage *(Symplocarpus foetidus)* is commonly found in damp soil where the forest borders a stream, pond, or wetland. It is one of the first plants to bloom in spring, sometimes as early as February, when the ground is still frozen and covered with snow. As the plant grows, it progresses through several transformations so radical that the leafy adult plant barely resembles its early flowering stage. Skunk cabbage begins its spring emergence as early as February, when it appears as a large mottled brownish purple and green spathe that encompasses a spadix with tiny inconspicuous flowers. The plant's beginnings look more like antelope horns pushing up through the ground than they do a flowering plant. The spathes emerge at a rapid rate and the heat of cellular respiration as new plant tissue

forms becomes so great that skunk cabbage can melt its way through snow and ice. One might wonder how pollination occurs, since bees have not emerged from hibernation in February and the plant is not wind pollinated. Skunk cabbage gives off a putrid odor that attracts early emerging flies. Some species of flies lay their eggs in decaying flesh where their young maggots hatch, feed, and metamorphose into adults. The skunk cabbage's putrid odor mimics rotten flesh, and as a fly moves from one flowering spathe to another it transfers pollen, resulting in fertilization.

In the center of what is today Nassau County, a vast prairie interrupts the lushness of the surrounding forests. The Hempstead Plains is a large, naturally occurring grassland that is not unlike the prairies of the Midwest: it originally occupied an area of up to sixty thousand acres. Its borders extended from near the Queens/Nassau county line in the west to the Suffolk/Nassau county line in the east. It is easy to see how the town of Plainview on the prairie's eastern border got its name. Near Plainview, the Hempstead Plains merged eastward into the oak-brush plains, while its western perimeter gave way to the Brooklyn-Queens barrens. The upland forests along the Ronkonkoma Moraine contained it to the north and the narrow band of hardwoods along the island's South Shore made up its southern border.

Formerly the Hempstead Plains contained a rich diversity of plants. Grasses were the dominant life-form here, but wildflowers held an important place as well. Small, scattered shrubs of various species shaded the grasses, but the entire area was absent of any

June-blooming mountain laurel *(Kalima latifolia)* and chestnut oak *(Quercus prinus)* grow along the dry ridge tops of the Harbor Hill Moraine in Stillwell Woods County Park, Nassau County.

The bird foot violet *(Viola pedata)* once covered the Hempstead Plains and, in early spring before the grasses greened, its flowers flushed the prairie with their violet hues. Today, few plants remain on the tiny fraction of surviving plains, but bird foot violets remain locally common throughout the pine barrens.

trees. Descriptions and old photographs clearly show the plains as an extensive prairie of waist-high grasses that spread to the horizon in all directions. Until World War II, there were still large tracts of prairie intact. My mother, who spent summers in Hicksville in the 1930s, remembers them well.

No one has ever presented a convincing explanation why the Hempstead Plains evolved into a prairie community. The plains exists on glacial outwash not unlike the outwash areas where the pine barrens grow. For reasons unknown, the pines could not survive here, possibly because the frequency of burns was too great even for them. Well-established prairies can tolerate yearly burns, and it appears that this was the case in the Hempstead Plains. Early descriptions of the flora note almost a total lack of fire-intolerant species. European farmers suppressed the fires, and shortly thereafter trees and shrubs crept into the prairie. Extensive grazing probably helped maintain the prairie community. Following World War II, suburban development gobbled up the plains at an alarming rate. The last vestiges are located in several parcels totaling no more than one hundred acres near Nassau Coliseum and nearby Eisenhower Park.

Of the many species of grasses that make up the Hempstead Plains, the most common is probably big blue stem grass *(Andropogon gerardi)*. At three to five feet tall, big blue stem is one of the taller grasses of the plains. Turkey foot grass is another name for the species; the seed heads, arranged in groups of three, resemble a turkey's foot. Little blue stem grass *(Andropogon scoparius)* is another grass of the plains and is also found along Long Island's seashore dunes. A late-spring sprouting grass whose

new stem bases have a bluish tint, little blue stem flowers late as well, usually in August or September, and its seeds are a favorite food of wintering birds. During the winter the previous year's growth turns a russet red color: bathed in dawn's light, a field of dormant little blue stem grass is the epitome of understated beauty. Indian grasses *(Sorghastrum spp.)* grow as tall as the big blue stem, but their spikelets (that is, their flowering parts) form a plumelike cluster. Other grasses of the plains include bent grasses *(Agrostis spp.)* and panic grasses *(Panicum spp.)*.

Multitudes of wildflowers grow among the grasses. Some remain discreetly hidden, while others boldly display their colorful blossoms. One of the first wildflowers to appear on the prairie, often before most of the grasses have sprouted, is the bird foot violet *(Viola pedata)*. These are small plants growing about six to ten inches high with deeply cut leaves reminiscent of a songbird's foot and light blue/violet flowers that grow on a separate stalk and usually appear in April or May. Bird foot violets were once prolific, and in spring their blossoms cloaked large expanses of the plains. Today, the spring show put on by the violets is not so ostentatious, but there are places in the pine barrens where they still grow in good numbers.

The unique character and growing conditions of the Hempstead Plains support some unusual plants. Recently discovered growing on one of the last remaining remnants of the plains was a population of sandplain gerardia *(Agalinis acuta)*. This is a very rare plant, almost indistinguishable from the common purple gerardia, with only nine known stations worldwide. Long Island is fortunate in having five of the nine sites, with most of the locations on the South Fork.

The lush profusion of wildflowers that graced the plains once supported an equally abundant population of butterflies. The regal fritillary (*Speyeria idalia*) was especially plentiful because its larval host plant was the bird foot violet. A big butterfly (about three and a half inches across), the regal fritillary was one of the most strikingly colored insects in our area. Its open upper wings are predominately orange and, in a striking contrast, the lower wings are black with an iridescent blue sheen and prominent white spots. Unfortunately the regal fritillary disappeared with the prairie and is no longer present on Long Island.

The plains were, of course, also an irresistible lure to the various species of birds that favor open habitat. Although the shore is a long way off, one of the more common birds nesting on the Hempstead Plains was, surprisingly, a shorebird. The large (about twelve inches long), plump upland sandpiper (*Bartramia longicauda*) has a relatively long neck, perhaps to help it see over the tall prairie grasses, and a small head; its large, dark eyes give its countenance an aura of youth. This lovely bird's preference for prairies and fields has unfortunately led to its near eradication on Long Island, as these habitats have all but disappeared. During spring migration, upland sandpipers sometimes show up along the barrier islands and, believe it or not, there remains a small breeding colony at John F. Kennedy International Airport in Queens. There, amid the roar of jet engines and the odor of aviation fuel, they breed each year along runways that are as prairielike a habitat as you will find for many miles. It is interesting to

observe that the upland sandpiper's limiting factor appears to be a very strict requirement in what type of land it nests on. The hustle and bustle of the airport runways do not seem to be of any concern.

At one time migrating shorebirds visited the plains in great numbers. Huge flocks of golden plovers (*Pluvialis squatarola*) and Eskimo curlews (*Numenius borealis*—now probably extinct) filled the skies, making easy targets for hunters who supplied local markets. Today, the only shorebird that regularly nests on the remnants of the plains is the killdeer (*Charadrius vociferus*). Killdeers are common on Long Island, especially at beaches, where they breed along the grass shoulders that line the drives. A far more adaptable species than the upland sandpiper, killdeer will breed anywhere there is an open grassy field. A pair fledges young every year in the field of my daughter's elementary school in the quiet suburban town of Merrick. This large brown bird (about ten inches long) has a white breast and two black necklacelike bands across the neck. If you can get a close look, you will notice fleshy red rings around their big dark eyes. Killdeer are very vocal during the breeding season, and most people notice them because of the ruckus they make when their nests are threatened. Many shorebirds employ elaborate distraction techniques to keep predators away from their young and killdeers probably do it best. A bird protecting a nest will often feign a broken wing while uttering cries of pain and flashing a rust-colored rump patch to catch a predator's attention. When the intruder goes for the adult, it will run off a short distance and repeat the display. In this fashion, the predator is lured away from the nest or the young.

Several species of grassland sparrow were once common breeders on the Hempstead Plains. The grasshopper sparrow (*Ammodramus savannarum*) is a fairly nondescript brownish bird with a funny-shaped head. Most birds have a rounded head; the grasshopper sparrow looks as if the top part of its head had been

neatly shaved, giving it a flat top. It has an equally strange variety of calls, one of which resembles the high-pitched buzz of a grasshopper. In the late 1920s, one observer noted about one hundred pairs nesting in the Hempstead Plains. By the 1940s, he estimated around twenty pairs, and this trend of decline has continued to today. Grasshopper sparrows occasionally breed in selected sites across the island, but the remaining Hempstead Plains seems too small to support a breeding population. The vesper sparrow (*Pooecetes gramineus*), another ground-nesting bird, at one time had an immense presence on the Hempstead Plains. These are birds of prairies and farms, and for a while small numbers persisted in the farmlands of eastern Suffolk. Their status today is uncertain.

Upland sandpipers
(*Bartramia longicauda*) are shorebirds that prefer to nest in open, prairielike settings. The original sixty thousand acres of prairie that we call the Hempstead Plains provided nesting habitat to perhaps the East's greatest numbers, but habitat destruction has eliminated them as breeders there. A small group breeds each year in the prairielike runway margins at John F. Kennedy International Airport in Queens. Occasionally, migrating upland sandpipers like this one, seen in a field of dandelions at Robert Moses State Park in Suffolk County, turn up on Long Island.

Overleaf:
The Hempstead Plains
were the largest naturally occurring grassland east of the Mississippi River, but presently less than one hundred acres of a once-sixty-thousand-acre prairie remain. This view shows a small part of the remaining prairie owned by Nassau County near the Nassau Coliseum.

CHAPTER 6

THE PINE BARRENS AND
THE DWARF PINE BARRENS

The pine barrens ecosystem makes up the majority of Long Island's interior landmass and originally covered more than 250,000 acres before the arrival of European settlers. Pressures of development since that time have taken their toll, and currently only about 100,000 acres remain, with 60 percent of the loss having occurred since 1940. The bulk of the pine barrens is centrally located in Suffolk County and comprises the last great undeveloped parcel of land on Long Island. Parts of this tract, dominated by oaks and known as the oak-brush plains, extend into eastern Nassau County. Other tracts of pine barrens occur on the South Fork, and a thin prong extends along the South Shore from Suffolk County westward into Nassau County. The pine barrens ecosystem is dominated by pitch pine (*Pinus rigida*), scrub oak (*Quercus ilicifolia*), and dwarf oak (*Quercus prinoides*), all hardy plants whose special adaptations allow them to thrive in the inhospitable growing conditions found there.

During the last period of glaciation there were several advances and retreats of ice to the Long Island region. Each episode resulted in the deposition of material suspended by the glacier as the ice melted. These deposits account for almost all of Long Island's current geological features. The final movements of the last great episode of glaciation, the Wisconsin glacial advance, sent streams of sediment-laden water southward into the Atlantic Ocean. The water flowed in broad fan-shaped patterns called alluvial fans and deposited layers of gravel and sand in a huge outwash plain, forming the bulk of the central and southern Long Island landmass. The outwash plain consists of a fine silica sand with little organic material, layered over a strata of coarse sand and gravel. The geology of this outwash plain steered the course of the developing ecosystems that formed there as the ice age faded and present climatic conditions developed. The sand and gravel substrate of the outwash plain is acidic, nutrient poor, and extremely dry. Water simply percolates through the porous ground, accumulating in vast subterranean pools called aquifers. A very special community of plants has evolved in this desertlike environment.

Some eleven thousand years ago, boreal forests of jack pine (Pinus banksiana) and spruce (Picea) colonized the outwash plain. The glaciers hastened their retreat as the climate continued to warm, and about eight thousand years ago pitch pine established itself on the outwash plain, replacing the jack pine and spruces. The pine barrens ecosystem is one of the rarest and most unusual plant and animal communities known, with only twenty occurrences

around the world. Most examples are in the eastern United States, with the New Jersey pine barrens being the largest. The Albany Pine Bush and parts of the Shawangunk Mountains in New York are others. The name "pine barrens" is misleading, as the barrens are quite lush with vegetation. It probably arose from the observation that cultivation of cash crops consistently failed in the poor soil, hence the term "barrens." The pine barrens are inhospitable to all but plants with special adaptations for life in a desiccating, nutrient-poor environment. Many plants surviving in this habitat, like plants on the barrier islands, exhibit phenotypes that allow for the retention of water. Thick succulent leaves that hold moisture is one adaptation. A protective waxy coating on the upper surface of leaves that acts as a barrier to water vapor evaporating from the leaf surface is another.

The pine forests are relatively open, allowing sunshine to penetrate to the forest floor. Solar radiation gives rise to a ground temperature as much as twenty degrees warmer than in a deciduous upland forest ecosystem. The acidic condition of the soil stifles the growth of decomposing organisms, and leaf litter and other organic material tend to accumulate into dry heaps of kindling. Consequently, pine barrens are vulnerable to fire (usually, in nature, caused by lightning), which has become the major force in maintaining the integrity of this unusual habitat. Fire consumes this dry environment about once every twenty-five years in most places and as often as once every five to six years in the dwarf pine barrens. Therefore, pine barrens vegetation must be able to withstand frequent burns and to colonize burnt areas expediently. It is not so much that pine barrens vegeta-

tion requires poor, dry soil and fire to thrive as much as it requires these conditions to keep other types of plants from invading its domain. In areas where there has not been a burn in a very long time, species atypical of the pine barrens get a foothold. Without the weeding-out process that fire provides, the composition of the barrens would be forever altered.

Pitch pine is the most fire-resistant tree in the Northeast and therefore it is the dominant tree in Long Island's pine barrens. Pitch pines can grow to forty to sixty feet with a diameter of one to two feet; few attain this height on Long Island. With needles one and a half to five inches long in bundles of three, it is the only three-needled pine on Long Island, and its field identification is relatively easy. Its thick bark is broken into irregularly shaped protective plates that insulate the cambium, the growth layer, from all but the hottest fires. Following a blaze, mature pitch pines will exhibit new growth originating from meristematic tissue in between the bark plates, known as epicormic branching. These new shoots will quickly replace branches seared by the last fire. Trees that have survived many fires take on a curious twisted shape as a result of having their crowns burnt several times and the repeated growth of horizontal epicormic branches along their lower trunk. Young trees totally consumed by flames aboveground are able to generate new shoots from their root systems. Many plants that thrive in the barrens have well-developed root systems that store large quantities of plant starch and act as an energy storehouse for regeneration after a fire. Typically pine barrens blazes run quickly along the ground, destroying dry grass, shrubs, and any invading nonbarrens vegetation unable to survive even a brief exposure to fire.

There are two groups of seed-producing plants: angiosperms and gymnosperms. Angiosperms include flowering plants whose seeds form inside a protective chamber called an ovary. Pitch pines are gymnosperms, which are vascular plants whose seeds, referred to as naked, do not develop in an enclosed chamber. There are both male and female cones on each pitch pine, and they display a striking dimorphism (that is, their forms are different). The male cones are small, cigar shaped, and grow in bunches on the pine's lower branches. Their life span is short, about four weeks, which is just enough time to release copious amounts of pollen in spring and subsequently atrophy and die. Pollen contains the male gametophytes necessary for sexual reproduction. The female cones grow singularly and are rounder and larger than the male cones. Female cones primed for reproduction have open slits between their cone scales to allow the entry of pollen, which is carried from the male by wind. Wind gusts jarring a pollinating pine will cause the male cones to fill the air with clouds of pollen, ensuring pollination with all the female cones. This is a fascinating event to witness, as long as you do not suffer from hay fever. Female cones require two years to produce viable seeds: they have numerous scales, each containing two ovules, and each ovule contains a nucellus capable of producing a seed. During the first year, a pollen grain, now lodged in the female cone, germinates and forms a pollen tube that eventually digests its

way through the nucellus that houses the female gametophyte. It takes a year or longer for the male gametophyte to reach the female and for fertilization to occur. During the second year the fertilized embryo develops into a winged seed, usually released to the winds in autumn.

Below the pitch pines, the understory of the pine barrens is dominated by a number of shrubby plants. Scrub oak and dwarf oak are two bushy species of oak that often form dense thickets anywhere from two to nine feet high. Scrub oak has leaves two to five inches long with deeply cut lobes and a woolly white underside, while the dwarf oak's leaves lack the lobes and have sharply toothed edges. These oaks can recover from fire even more quickly than pitch pines. Their larger relatives, the white, scarlet, and black oaks, can only tolerate burns at intervals of ten to twenty years, but the scrub and dwarf oak can withstand many more. The forest composition can be an indicator of how often fire ravages an area. Areas where pitch pines dominate the canopy are more frequently burned than areas with large oaks or other deciduous species of trees. Regions dominated by scrub oaks with few pitch pines endure more fires than pitch-pine canopied areas. The oak-brush plains located in central western Suffolk and eastern Nassau counties is such an area. It marks the transition zone from the pine barrens proper to the Hempstead Plains further west, which can tolerate yearly burn cycles. The New York State Edgewood Oak-Brush Plains Preserve in Edgewood is the largest remaining example of this transition community left. The grounds of nearby Pilgrim State Psychiatric Hospital is another fine example of oak-brush plains.

Other plants common to the pine barrens understory include members of the heath family (Ericaceae). Most heaths have adaptations, such as thick leathery leaves, that allow them to tolerate the dry conditions of the pine barrens. They also thrive in acid soils and can survive the fires that periodically sweep the region. The heaths are a large and diverse family, well represented on Long Island, and include many familiar and economically important members, as well as a few unusual species. Low bush blueberry (Vaccinium vacillans) and the almost identical late low blueberry (Vaccinium angustifolium) are ubiquitous throughout the pine barrens. Their berries are quite small, diminutive to a small garden pea, but their sweet taste easily overshadows their tiny size. Blueberries ripen by late June to early July and are among the great treats that the pine barrens have to offer. Huckleberries are another common heath of the pine barrens and strongly resemble the blueberries. One way to separate the two is to check for tiny, yellow, resinous dots on new leaves and twigs, present in huckleberries only. Huckleberry fruit is sweet and edible but differs from blueberries in that it has a tougher outer covering and contains many small seeds. Like blueberries there are several species of huckleberry that strongly resemble each other, making identification challenging. Black huckleberry (Gaylussacia baccata) is probably the most widespread; it gets to be about three feet high and its fruit is dark, almost black. The other common huckleberry is the dwarf huckleberry (Gaylussacia dumosa); as its name suggests, it grows close to the ground.

A mature pitch pine (Pinus rigida) near the shore of Hubbard Creek.

Staggerbush (*Lyonia mariana*) is, at seven feet, another shrubby member of the heath family. It superficially resembles the blueberries and huckleberries, but there are noticeable differences. Most notably its pink to white urn-shaped flowers produce a five-parted fruit that remains on the plant throughout the winter and into spring as dried capsules. Sheep laurel (*Kalima angustifolia*) is probably the most beautiful of all the pine barrens' heaths. It is a low shrub reaching a height of two to three feet with narrow leaves about two inches long in whorls of three. In June, small cup-shaped pink flowers no more than half an inch across adorn the plant, adding a splash of color to the monotonous green hues of the pine barrens' heath understory. Sheep laurel is also called lambkill because it can be poisonous if grazed upon. Unfortunately sheep laurel is not overly abundant in the pine barrens. A good area to find it is in the eastern portion of the Manorville Hills near Riverhead. This is an interesting area where the Ronkonkoma Moraine passes through the pine barrens, creating a rugged maze of steep hills and deep hollows. Bald Hill, just north of Moriches Riverhead Road, is, at 295 feet, the region's high point and offers views eastward toward Flander's Bay and Peconic Bay and south to the Atlantic. Other nearby hills offer lookouts over a green sea of twisted pitch pines only occasionally broken by the speckled highlights of a kettle pond. This is the largest area of undeveloped land left on Long Island and, together with the west Manorville Hills, encompasses more than sixty-four hundred acres. It is possible to walk along paths and old tote roads all day in the realm of the forest without ever coming across Long Island's

pervasive suburban constructions. It is one of the only places left on the island where you can still obtain a feeling of solitude and primeval wilderness.

Some of the pine barrens' heaths have prostrate growth habits. Bearberry (*Arctostaphylos uva-ursi*) hugs the ground, no more than a foot high, with evergreen leaves and woody branches that grow outward from its center, often forming sizable mats. Because bearberry requires direct sunlight, it grows along woodland edges and in areas, like old burns or disturbed areas, where shade-producing plants are absent. It has white or pink bell-shaped flowers that appear in April and are followed by red fruit in summer. The fruit looks very much like cranberries, but if you try one you will notice the similarity ends there. Bearberry fruit, although edible, is not palatable to humans, being mealy and tasteless. The plant's scientific species name, meaning "bears grape" in Latin, suggests that this is a favorite food of wildlife. I have never seen any living thing eat a bearberry, and, furthermore, the plants usually have good numbers of berries on them throughout winter and into spring, indicating sparse utilization. Nevertheless, the ubiquitous nature of the plant throughout the pine barrens and Long Island's beaches suggests that wildlife uses this as a food crop and perhaps as a last resort starvation food. Being resistant to the low pH, acidic environment of mammalian and avian stomachs, seeds within the berries spread to new locations as they pass through an animal's digestive tract. The stomach acid does have some effect: it seems to weaken the seed's outer coat just enough to permit germination.

Another ground-covering heath typical of the pine barrens is wintergreen (*Gaultheria procumbens*).

The white-tailed deer (*Odocoileus virginianus*) is without question the pine barren's largest and most visible mammal.

Opposite:
A woodland of pitch pines and oaks in Flanders County Park.

Overleaf:
Long Island's pine barrens cover one hundred thousand acres on Long Island and are characterized by woodlands of pitch pines (*Pinus rigida*) with an understory of heaths.

Sheep laurel (*Kalima angustifolia*), a small member of the heath family found in the pine barrens, bursts into bloom in mid-June.

Opposite:
Bearberry (*Arctostaphylos uva-ursi*), huckleberries (*Gaylussacia*), and blooming stiff aster (*Aster linariifolius*) decorate the forest floor in autumn along a high moranial ridge in the pine barrens near Riverhead.

Overleaf:
Scarlet oaks (*Quercus coccinea*) have become the dominant tree in some areas of the pine barrens. Where fire has been suppressed, other more aggressive species of trees will eventually replace the pitch pines.

It creeps along the ground, spreading by underground stems and forming attractive colonies of waxy, oval green leaves. In April, nodding, white bell-shaped flowers appear that produce a red berry by autumn. Crush the leaves or eat the edible fruit of wintergreen and you will understand why early European settlers used the extract to flavor gum, candy, medicine, and tea. Another low-growing evergreen heath is the trailing arbutus (*Epigaea repens*). Trailing arbutus has leathery, oval leaves with hairy margins and, in April, white or pink flowers with a fragrance that can vary from plant to plant, some having a strong, sweet odor like cheap perfume and others only mildly scented. Arbutus cannot tolerate being covered by leaf litter and favors open, sunny areas: it grows almost exclusively along sloping trail edges and road cuts throughout the pine barrens.

Of course, not every plant growing in the pine barrens' understory is a heath. The evergreen shrub inkberry (*Ilex glabra*) is a member of the same genus as American holly (*Ilex opaca*), although superficially they do not resemble one another at all. American holly has distinctive wavy and curled leaves with small, prickled teeth and colorful fruit, while inkberry's leaves are generally toothless and narrow, with a little notch at the end of a blunt tip, and the black fruit is inconspicuous. American holly is most common in Long Island's maritime forests, while inkberry favors the pine barrens, although you occasionally find each in the other's preferred habitat.

Surprisingly the poor soils of the pine barrens contain numerous wildflower species. Cow wheat (*Melampyrum lineare*) is an annual member of the snapdragon (*Scrophulariaceae*) family that blooms in early summer. The tubular flower looks like the tiny open mouth of a hungry salamander waiting for a meal: the white, arched, upper lip has two lobes, while the lower lip is three-lobed and yellow. Cow wheat is usually found in the pine barrens uplands, where the pitch pines are dominant and fairly large. Blue toadflax (*Linaria canadensis*), with tiny blue flowers scattered along a slender stem, is another member of the snapdragon family that grows in the dry soil of the pine barrens uplands. Toadflax, which is usually in bloom in early summer but sometimes as late as September, grows anywhere the soil is poor and dry, such as our beaches and waste places. Sickle-leafed golden aster (*Chyrsopsis falcata*) is a late-summer blooming species. It is common in disturbed open areas, where its small clusters of terminal yellow flowers speckle the landscape with bright flashes of color. When not in bloom, the low-growing plants often go unnoticed. Their sickle-shaped leaves and hairy stems are adaptations that help conserve water.

Some of the showiest wildflower species in the pine barrens are members of the pea family (*Leguminosae*), of which many different species occur. June-flowering wild indigo (*Baptisia tinctoria*) is a bushy perennial herb with terminal clusters of bright yellow, pea-shaped flowers arranged in racemes at the branch tip. A superior specimen is as attractive as any cultivated flower at your local nursery. Wild indigo's stalkless leaves turn a deep blue-black when dried, accounting for the plant's Greek genus name *baptizein*, meaning "to dye." Native Americans and early European settlers extracted a blue dye from the leaves of wild indigo. A similar plant of the pine barrens is American goat's rue (*Tephrosia virginiana*). Like wild indigo, goat's rue is a bushy member of the pea family, but unlike wild indigo it has bicolored flowers. Pea flowers have five petals: a wide upper petal, called the banner, two side petals, called wings, and two lower petals, called keels. Goat's rue has pink wings and a yellow banner, giving it a very festive look. Fine, silky hairs cover its stems, helping to reduce desiccation and giving the plant an overall shiny look. Goat's rue was once fed to goats to boost milk production, but this practice stopped when it became apparent that the plant contains rotenone, a poisonous compound. Another common name for goat's rue is devil's shoestrings, which refers to the plant's extensive network of roots, which helps it gather water from the sandy soil and regenerate after a fire. The blue lupine (*Lupinus perennis*) is another handsome legume, for the most part restricted to the pine barrens on Long Island. Lupines appear as scattered plants here and there, but many areas lack them altogether; conversely a few select

sites contain hundreds of plants. They, too, have pea-shaped flowers and bloom in early summer—the blossoms are as blue as the sky.

Numerous other legumes thrive in the pine barrens, and you may wonder why. Like the pitch pines, legumes have special, although different, adaptations, allowing them to survive in the harsh growing conditions of the pine barrens where other plants would fail. Plants in the legume family are capable of nitrogen fixation, that is, of changing atmospheric nitrogen in the form of N_2 into ammonia (NH_3). Nitrogen is an element integral to all living things, being an essential ingredient in proteins and nucleic acids. Eighty percent of the earth's atmosphere is nitrogen, but most of it is unavailable to plants because atmospheric nitrogen is in a gaseous form, and plants can only absorb nitrogen when it is in the chemical form of ammonium or nitrate.

The nitrogen available to plants is mostly locked up in decaying organic matter—leaf litter and so forth. Various bacteria in the soil play an essential role in recycling this nitrogen. Ammonifying bacteria, on the one hand, break down organic matter, creating ammonium, which is useful to growing plants. Denitrifying bacteria, on the other hand, convert ammonium and nitrates back to gaseous nitrogen, which diffuses from the soil into the atmosphere. (There are also nitrogen-fixing bacteria that can change atmospheric nitrogen into useful ammonium.) These processes require a great deal of energy, and such bacteria are likely to be found in soil rich in organic material that can provide fuel for cellular respiration. Pine barrens soil, however, is poor and hostile to life, including ammonifying bacteria and other decom-

posers, and consequently the amount of useful nitrogen available to plants is low.

Legumes have evolved an ingenious method for dealing with this problem. Their roots have swollen nodules, easily visible if you yank one up out of the ground, which contain specialized plant cells that harbor nitrogen-fixing bacteria. The bacteria is of the genus *Rhizobium*, which means "root living," and within the nodules take on a special form called a bacteroid. Curiously each species of legume is partnered with a different species of *Rhizobium*. Both the plant and bacteria benefit from their symbiotic relationship, with the bacteria supplying nitrogen to the plant and the plant supplying nutrients to the bacteria. Incredibly the complexity and elegance of this relationship is not unique. Countless examples of the intricacies of life surround us in all living things in all places, and one of the great privileges of human life is being able to discover and understand them.

The green plants of the pine barrens, like photosynthetic organisms in almost every other ecosystem on Earth, provide the conduit that transfers energy from the sun to the pine barrens' animals. One creature directly dependent on the pine barrens' flora for food and shelter is the white-tailed deer *(Odocoileus virginianus)*. Deer usually spend the dusk hours feeding and the rest of the time hidden among the brush, where they rest and chew their cud. They are herbivores and feed exclusively on plants, but the cellulose that provides the structure of every plant cell is not digestible by any mammal on Earth. Like the legumes, deer have solved this problem by evolving a symbiotic relationship with bacteria. The deer's digestive system has an elaborate multichambered foregut

that processes food before it reaches the intestines for absorption. The part of the foregut that houses bacteria capable of breaking down cellulose is called the rumen. Food in the rumen is fermented and then regurgitated, rechewed, and reswallowed by the deer in an efficient cycle that breaks down plant fibers into smaller pieces, increasing the surface area available to the bacteria and allowing for almost total extraction of nourishment from the plant cells. (Deer and other animals whose digestive systems process cellulose in this manner are called "ruminants.") Eventually the regurgitated food, now called "cud," moves to the intestine, where it is absorbed along with great numbers of the bacteria that actually supply the deer with a substantial part of its nutrition. Fortunately the bacteria reproduce at such a high rate that the rumen is always populated with enough to handle digestion of the cud.

White-tailed deer are ubiquitous throughout the pine barrens. You can see them along roads, where they come to browse succulent grasses, and their hoof prints are everywhere in the sandy soil, especially along the footpaths and dirt tracks that offer deer, as well as humans, the path of least resistance while traversing the region. Deer also create and utilize a system of trails of their own making by traveling the same routes over and over again. Their hoof print appears as a heart broken into two parts, with the pointed apex indicating the direction of travel. When conditions are favorable, such as in fresh snow or mud, a small imprint is left behind each part: these are the dew claws. Sometimes, following a deer trail will lead to a sheltered area where the deer bed down. Their scat, usually piles of small, dry, dark pellets, is another distinctive sign of their presence.

Bucks and does ordinarily remain segregated throughout the year. Bucks are solitary or form small groups, while the does and fawns maintain larger congregations. Only during the autumn breeding season, known as the rut, do the sexes have any sustained interaction. In spring, bucks begin to grow antlers in preparation for the rut. Antlers are solid bony structures that grow from pedicles on the buck's skull. The integument (skin) covers the antlers as they grow, supplying the structure with blood and offering protection. This growth, known as velvet because of its textural resemblance to that fabric, shrivels and dies when the antlers mature in September. Bucks hasten the shedding of their velvet by thrashing their heads into bushes. If you ever witness this sight, you will observe a messy affair complete with blood and what appears as more than minor discomfort for the buck. Antlers are primarily a device for intraspecific aggression during the rut. The rigors of head ramming between bucks during this time eventually determines who will breed and pass on their genetic makeup to the next generation. In this way natural selection, the primary mechanism of evolution, ensures that subsequent generations will be best prepared to survive within their environment. Bucks shed their antlers in late winter to renew the cycle the following spring.

There are other mammalian denizens within the pine woods besides deer, but most are nocturnal, secretive, and seldom seen. The eastern mole (Scalopus aquaticus) is a small mammal that is almost never seen, but the network of tunnels it digs cannot help but be noticed. These moles are small, only three to eight inches long, with gray fur that has a velvety quality to it. They are almost totally subterranean creatures, only rarely breaking the surface and spending their days tunneling in search of earthworms and grubs. Their life underground has lifted the evolutionary pressure to maintain vision; consequently they lack eyes. Adaptations that include large shovel-like forefeet for tunneling and a long hairless nose that can sensitively probe for prey superbly enable moles to carry out their lifestyle. A life underground may not seem very desirable, but in the pine barrens the greatest diversity of life occurs below the ground because moisture and temperature levels remain fairly constant there.

A tunneling mole may on occasion cross paths with another infamous burrowing organism of the pine barrens, the hognose snake (Heterodon platyrhinos). Hognose snakes range from twenty to forty-five inches in length and have thick bodies and a peculiar upturned snout. Their color is variable, ranging from brown to yellow to gray, with dark square marks on their back and a row of dark round dorsolateral spots on each side. They are mostly nocturnal, but are often active during the day, foraging through the pine woods in search of Fowler's toads, their favorite prey. They are commonly called puff adders, in reference to their elaborate behavior when threatened. When agitated they will inflate their neck and body and hiss and strike an aggressor. If this fails to ward off a predator, they will roll over and play dead. They do an excellent job of this, becoming totally limp and sticking their tongue out the side of their mouth. Unfortunately hognose snake numbers have been severely reduced on Long Island. The reasons are unclear. Hognose numbers fluctuate with the population of toads in an area, and since Fowler's toads have been decreasing on Long Island (although they are still plentiful), this might be an explanation. Additionally, fragmentation of available habitat, primarily by roads, proves to be a deadly obstacle to snakes, as well as to other reptiles and amphibians, that at times need to transverse them. A snake crossing the open expanse of a busy two-lane highway is not a good bet to survive.

The black racer (Coluber constrictor) is another native snake once common but now rarely seen. The large, undisturbed expanses of the pine barrens are your best place to run into one on Long Island. Black racers are slender and long and capable of reaching a length of more than seventy inches. Despite their scientific name, these snakes do not kill their prey by constriction. They are diurnal hunters that swiftly patrol the pine woods with their head held high, ready to strike at unsuspecting prey. Black racers move very quickly and, more often than not, that swishing sound you hear in the underbrush is a racer getting out of your way. If you can manage to grab one, it will strike repeatedly until released. As a warning when cornered, a black racer will rattle its tail in dry leaves, making a buzzing noise not unlike a rattlesnake. It's best to heed the warning.

The pine barrens are not as rich in avian life as some of Long Island's other habitats, yet they do provide a home for both common and a few unusual nesting species of birds. Typically many of the pine barrens' breeding birds are those species that prefer scrubby growth. The rufous-sided towhee (Pipilo erythropthalmus) is such a

Prairie warblers (*Dendroica discolor*) are common breeding birds in Long Island's pine barrens. This prairie warbler is feeding on insects attracted to blooming beach plums in Jones Beach State Park.

Adult black racers (*Coluber constrictor*) are black above and white on the belly. In contrast, the young are gray with dark reddish brown marks running down their backs and look so different from the adults that you would think they were a different species. In fact, they resemble the milk snake (*Lampropeltis triangulum*), another native Long Island reptile, more closely than their own adult species.

bird, spending a great deal of its day in scrubby growth or on the forest floor. Towhees scratch the leaf litter with a comical little backward hop, accomplished by moving both feet simultaneously and, in so doing, they expose seeds and insects taking refuge from the hot sun. Towhees are members of the sparrow family, but, unlike Long Island's other sparrow species, towhees are beautifully colored. They have brilliant red eyes (their scientific species name comes from the Greek *erythros*, meaning red, and *ophthalmos*, for eye) and a band of brick-red feathers along their sides, giving rise to their common name, "rufous sided." Basically the males and females look alike, except that the male's head, back, and tail are shiny black, while the female's are a subdued brown. This sexual differentiation relates to the job that each performs during the breeding season. Towhees construct their nest on the ground out of grasses, twigs, and leaves. The female handles the nest construction and most of the incubation, and her brown coloring offers her camouflage from predators while performing these activities.

Brown thrashers (*Toxostoma rufum*) are reddish-brown birds with black-streaked, white breasts that are at home in dry thickets. Thrashers are large for songbirds, with a wingspan close to fourteen inches. The males are very vocal and commonly choose a high spot where they perch erect with tail drooping down and sing their song, which is a series of musical phrases, each repeated twice. The song is somewhat similar to that of the mockingbird (*Mimus polyglottos*), a close relative of the thrasher.

While walking through the pine barrens in June, you might hear an odd buzzing sound composed

of a series of identical, but separate, notes rising in pitch. It is reminiscent of the calls of attacking giant insects from 1950s science-fiction movies, but this buzzing call belongs to the prairie warbler (*Dendroica discolor*). Prairie warblers are small migratory birds that, in spite of their common name, like to nest in scrub and pine woods, and the pine barrens are the only place where they breed on Long Island. They are handsome little birds with olive-green backs and yellow breasts with black streaks on the side. They have an odd habit of twitching their tails when they move about, giving them a very neurotic appearance.

Another bird that, on Long Island, lives exclusively in the pine barrens is the ruffed grouse (*Bonasa umbellus*). A ruffed grouse is a large fowl-like bird, and a reasonable description would be to call it a wild chicken. For the most part, these grouse are gray, with both light and dark speckles and bands on most of the feathers. Their tail feathers are multibanded with dark terminal ends, and they have a ruff of dark feathers that normally lie flat around their necks. When a grouse becomes excited, it can raise the erectile feathers of its ruff and crown, creating a stunning display. There exists two color phases of ruffed grouse, a gray phase and a red phase, with the difference mostly evident in the tail feathers. Normally the red race occupies the southern part of the grouse's range, while northern birds are gray, but mixing of races does occur. On Long Island, I have only seen the gray phase. In early spring, the males engage in fascinating behavior in order to attract a mate. After finding a suitable spot, usually a fallen log or an old stump, a male will hop on top and begin drumming. A grouse's drumming is homologous to a warbler's song and, like songbirds, grouse use the sound of drumming to establish territory and attract mates. The drumming sounds at first as if someone is beating a tom-tom, growing to a loud and fast-booming drum roll before abruptly stopping. The birds produce this sound in a very interesting way. The male grasps the drumming log firmly with his feet and braces himself, using its tail (the same log is sometimes used year after year by succeeding males and often shows wear from their claws). He then beats his wings toward his breast to produce the sound. Initially scientists believed that the wings actually hit the breast, but slow-motion photography has shown that the wings fall short. The sound is apparently generated by the cupped wings moving air rapidly. At the crescendo of drumming, the wings beat at a rate of twenty strokes per second. The sound is of a very low frequency and characteristically travels far; humans can hear a grouse drumming a quarter mile away. The male is polygamous: after attracting and mating with one female, his responsibilities to her are complete, and he will continue drumming to try his luck again.

The ruffed grouse had a cousin on Long Island but sadly that relative is no longer here. The heath hen (*Tympanuchus cupido*), a subspecies of the Midwestern greater prairie chicken, once lived throughout the sandy regions of the pine barrens, as well as the Hempstead Plains, but it is now extinct. The last prairie chicken found was on Martha's Vineyard in 1932, but by the 1830s or 1840s it had already become extinct on Long Island. There have been several reasons given for its demise, including overhunting and uncon-

trolled fires, but disease may have also played a role.

A happier fate has been assigned to the wild turkey (*Meleagris gallopavo*). Turkeys were once common on Long Island, but their numbers have dwindled, as populations were reduced by hunting and other human disturbance. They have recently been making a comeback, however, particularly in the central pine barrens. There is a large population in Connetquot River State Park, a legacy of the area's former history as a rod and reel club. By day, wild turkeys forage on the ground for nuts and insects; they spend the night roosting in trees. Turkeys are the largest native game birds in North America. The males are larger than the females and have iridescent body feathers, red wattles, and a black breast tuft that looks like a small ponytail hanging off their chest. All of these strange features come into play during the spring breeding season, when males engage in elaborate courtship dances. Their famous gobbling echoes through the woods at this time as the males compete for a chance to breed.

The pine barrens are host to several northern-breeding species of birds that normally only visit Long Island as transitory migrants or winter visitors. The hermit thrush (*Catharus guttatus*), which, in the eastern United States, breeds generally to the north of Long Island or southward only in the mountains, manages to breed each year in the pine barrens. It represents a Nearctic species existing on Long Island's piece of the coastal plain. This is another example of the mixing of northern and southern species of life that makes Long Island's natural history so interesting. The flutelike song of the hermit thrush is one of the most beautiful sounds in the spring woods. Hermit thrushes

have an olive-brown back and head and a white breast, with a buffy upper part and indistinct black spots. Their tail is reddish and, like the prairie warbler, they flick it up and down.

Other northern breeding birds that have nested on occasion in the pine barrens are the winter wren (*Troglodytes troglodytes*) and the brown creeper (*Certhia americana*). The tiny (it is no more than four inches long) winter wren has a short stumpy tail, as if the bird experienced a horrific accident. These birds are fond of skulking around in wood piles and brush, and consequently they usually go unseen, but their incredibly loud song always gives away their presence. Brown creepers are just a little larger than the winter wren,

Wild turkey (*Meleagris gallopavo*) were common in Long Island's forests, but overhunting eliminated most by the turn of the century; in recent years, their numbers have been increasing, especially in the pine barrens. These three turkeys are part of a large number of birds that roam free in Connetquot River State Park, which was formerly a hunting club where game birds were bred.

The hermit thrush (*Catharus guttatus*) is a songbird of northern woodlands that breeds in small numbers in Long Island's pine barrens. It is another example of the mixing of northern and southern species that occurs on Long Island.

with a decurved bill and a stiff tail that they use to brace themselves against a tree trunk. They feed by flying toward the base of a tree and then spiraling up the trunk while checking for insects. Brown creepers, although very rare breeders, visit Long Island each year as winter residents and even frequent suburban yards where there are large trees.

Within the pine barrens there is a small area encompassing about twenty-five hundred acres that supports an aberrant growth pattern of pine barrens vegetation. The dominant plants in the dwarf pine barrens are pitch pine and scrub oak, just as in the rest of the pine barrens, but the trees are stunted. Here, the pitch pines rarely exceed five or six feet, and many remain only a few feet high despite a lifetime of growth. The dwarf pine barrens is one of the rarest plant communities on Earth, with only two other examples known, one in the New Jersey pine barrens and the other in New York's Shawangunk Mountains.

Long Island's dwarf pine community occupies an area in Westhampton where Sunrise Highway and County Road 31 cross. Driving along Sunrise Highway from the west, the border between normal pine barrens growth and dwarf pines is abrupt and obvious. For reasons still not explained, the height of the trees becomes suddenly truncated, as if the entire area received an unwanted crew cut. Other, more subtle, differences exist as well. Normal pitch pines have cones that open each autumn and release seeds without any external stimuli. Dwarf pitch pine cones are serotinous, meaning that they require the stimuli of fire to melt the thick resin that closes shut the cone's scales. This adaptation wonderfully suits the

dwarf pine's morphology and survival in this strange area. The dwarf pines are subject to the most frequent rate of burning for the entire pine barrens community: once every five or six years. Since the trees are so small, even a rapidly moving fire may obliterate the entire plant, including its precious seeds. The sealed, serotinous cones not only protect the seeds from a passing conflagration, but also open and deposit their seeds once the fire has passed. The fire-cleared brush and ash-covered soil are conducive to the germination and growth of the next generation of pines.

Frequent fires in the dwarf pines have left the tiny trees even more twisted and grotesquely shaped than in other parts of the barrens. In some spots, the dwarf plains resemble a Japanese bonsai garden, pruned by fire and stunted by the sandy dry soil. The whole region is forbidding and uninviting to animal life. Unsurprisingly, the dwarf pines do have a lower diversity of life than the rest of the pine barrens, but there do exist a number of creatures able to exploit this particular habitat. One of the most interesting forms of life found there is the buck moth.

The buck moth (Hemileuca maia) is an unusual insect, remarkably adapted to exploit the demanding conditions of the pine barrens. Long Island's buck moths are a unique subspecies of a much wider ranging population. They are about one and a half inches long and mostly black, with a broad white band crossing wings that have just a hint of yellow to them. While most moths fly by night, buck moths are diurnal. Unlike most Lepidoptera (butterflies and moths) species that emerge from metamorphosis in spring or summer, the buck moth begins its flight in October. The buck moths appear in autumn so

that their life cycle will synchronize with the yearly conditions of the pine barrens.

The fire season in the pine barrens lasts from February through May (although there is always a chance of fire until the rains come in the fall), and this period is followed by summer droughts. Buck moths emerge from their underground chambers in October, when rainfall is plentiful. They fly during the day to avoid evening temperatures that can dip below freezing. Their predominately dark wings help them absorb the sun's energy, and when sufficiently warm by midday they begin their activities. Females will usually rest on the stem of a scrub oak, their larval host plant, and emit a chemical calling card called a pheromone to attract a male. The pheromones' molecules can disperse over great distances, improving a female's ability to locate a male. The feathery antennae of the male are larger than the female's, and their greater surface area helps them to follow the pheromone trail. After mating occurs, the female lays a cluster of about two hundred eggs in tight rings stacked upon one another around the stem of an oak leaf. The eggs have a protective waxy coat that is resistant to desiccation and fire. The adults that have no ability to feed then die, having fulfilled their sole purpose of reproducing.

The eggs overwinter. In May, hundreds of tiny, spin-covered, black caterpillars hatch and begin to feed on the oaks. They remain in groups until midsummer, when the then two-inch caterpillars become solitary. This strategy lessens their likelihood of falling prey to predation. Their primary predators are, surprisingly, not birds but parasitic wasps and flies that lay their eggs under the skin of the buck moth larva. There the eggs hatch and the larva feed on the caterpillar's fat stores, eventually killing it. As the caterpillars grow, they shed their outer skin to make room for increased body size. The periods between these molts are called instars, and sometime in summer, following their sixth instar, they leave the oaks and burrow in the loose, sandy soil of the pine barrens. In underground chambers, they molt once more, and this time a hard pupal case encloses the organism. Now an amazing restructuring of the caterpillar takes place. Enzymatic activity selectively breaks down the caterpillar's functioning tissues, while cells that were quiescent in the larva begin to grow and differentiate into the adult buck moth. In October, the adults emerge, and the cycle begins once more.

Pupas will not hatch unless there is sufficient rainfall in autumn. To hatch during a drought would leave the buck moth population particularly vulnerable to fire. Pupas that fail to hatch during occasional autumn droughts remain viable until the following autumn, when conditions might be better. This odd life cycle protects the moth from the environment when it is at its harshest. In good years, hundreds of moths fly about during October's Indian summer. Were it not for the bright autumn colors of the heaths and oaks, one might think one was experiencing spring's renewal of life.

The dwarf pine barrens also provide habitat for two rare breeding birds on Long Island. The whip-poor-will (Caprimulgus vociferus) is a large (almost ten inches) gray-brown mottled bird with, as its species name points out, a vociferous call. Whip-poor-wills are members of the nightjar family, which are nocturnal birds with large mouths. They fly at night, catching insects on the wing with a mouth

that opens like a huge shovel, able to scoop their prey out of the sky. The males differ from females in that they have white margins on their tail feathers that they conspicuously display during aerial mating dances. They nest on the forest floor in open areas. The whip-poor-will gets its name from its call, which sounds like "whip-poor-will," with accents on the first and last syllables. Their cry is loud and persistent. One observer has counted 1,088 consecutive calls, but volleys of fifty to one hundred are typical. On more than one occasion I have camped close to nesting whip-poor-wills, and, speaking from experience, the thrill of their song quickly wears off after you realize you've been up all night listening to it.

The other rare bird that breeds in the dwarf pine barrens is the northern harrier (Circus cyaneus), a large bird of prey with a wingspan up to forty-eight inches across. Northern harriers used to be called marsh hawks because they were frequently observed hunting in salt marshes. They are birds of open country, fields, and marshlands that seldom fly high above the ground, which may explain why they find the stunted low forest of dwarf pines suitable for nesting. They have become rare breeders in New York State, and the dwarf pine barrens represents one of their only nesting sites on Long Island. Like some owls, they have a parabolic facial disk that helps them to locate their prey by the sounds it makes. They feed by day on rodents as well as birds, which they are adept at flushing from the scrub and catching with their sharp talons. Their distinctive silhouette when in flight makes them easy to identify: they hold their wings in a dihedral and have a very long tail that is normally unflared as they soar. Both sexes have a white

Buck moth (Hemileuca maia) larva hatch from an egg mass on the twig of a scrub oak in the dwarf pine barrens.

rump patch, but the smaller male is silver gray elsewhere, while the female is chocolate brown.

While strolling through the dwarf pine barrens you may come across an unusual type of stone with a smooth polished side and an opposite facet rough and unhoned. These are called ventifacts and are relics of the immediate postglacial environment on Long Island. As the glaciers receded, the broad outwash plains they left behind remained barren and windblown for some time before vegetation could gain a foothold. During this period exposed stones were subjected to the prevailing winds and the abrasive particles they carried, which sandblasted the sides of stones into a smooth highly polished surface. Occasionally ventifacts will exhibit two polished facets, indicating a change in direction of the prevailing winds during their ontogeny. Although ventifacts can be of any mineral content, most of the ones I have found have been composed of quartzite.

Overleaf:
In the dwarf pine barrens sunrise illuminates the fire red autumn leaves of huckleberries (Gaylussacia spp.).

Stunted pines and huckle-berries growing in a mat of bearberry *(Arctostaphylos uva-ursi)* compose a characteristic dwarf pine barrens landscape.

Bearberry is one of the few understory plants capable of thriving in the infertile sandy soil of the dwarf pine barrens, where it forms large mats.

The pitch pines *(Pinus rigida)* in the dwarf pine barrens characteristically develop twisted, bizarre shapes. Visible on this pine are many serotonous cones that require the stimulus of fire for them to open and disperse their seeds. The understory is dominated by scrub oak *(Quercus ilicifolia)*, the host plant of the endangered buck moth *(Hemileuca maia)*.

CHAPTER 7

PONDS, KETTLES, BOGS, AND SWAMPS

People who enter the pine barrens are usually struck by the sameness all around them. The pitch pines and their lush understory seem remarkably uniform, with only islands of water randomly disrupting their sea of brown and green. These ponds are the jewels of the dry and sandy barrens, offering an oasis for water-loving plants and animals and increasing the diversity of life. The legacy of glaciation left the pine barrens riddled with small kettles, most of them being vernal like the kettle ponds along the North Shore. Some are deep water-table ponds, such as Long Island's largest pond, Lake Ronkonkoma, and others are shallow coastal plain ponds. The wet areas of the barrens also include acid bogs and white cedar swamps.

Coastal plain ponds are among the most interesting phenomena of the pine barrens. Streams and springs or, in the case of vernal kettles, rainwater, feed most ponds, but coastal plain ponds, although augmented by rainfall, fill from a different source. Coastal plain ponds are sandy-bottomed bodies of water that are never more than a few feet deep. They are simply shallow scrapes in the landscape that intersect the water table in the area and reflect that in how much they fill. Their simplicity of ontogeny in no way reflects the complexity of living conditions that these ponds create for the local flora and fauna. The height of the water table in the pine barrens fluctuates in response to changing conditions from month to month, and this results in varying water levels for coastal plain ponds. They are usually at their fullest in spring, after the winter thaw, and, as the summer progresses, their water levels drop. Some coastal plain ponds dry out completely by summer's end, just like the vernal kettles, but others maintain year-round water. During wet years, the water table rises and the ponds may double or triple in size; conversely, drought years may reduce the ponds to sandy scrapes. As the water level fluctuates, the pond's margins may change from wet to dry and back again. A whole community of specialized life has evolved that is able to thrive in the unique microenvironments caused by such drastically changing conditions.

Long Island's finest example of coastal plain ponds is the Calverton Ponds in Manorville, just south of Calverton Naval Weapons Center. The diversity of life found there is outstanding, evident in the number of rare and endangered species present. The ponds and surrounding area harbor Long Island's highest concentration of such life.

The tranquil still waters of the coastal plain ponds are conducive to the growth of floating aquatic plants. The fragrant water lily (Nymphaea odorata) is an aquatic plant with large, flat leaves that float on the water's surface. Unlike most plants that have their stomata (the leaf pores that vent carbon dioxide and oxygen) on the bottom, water lilies have stomata on top so that the leaves may float and still function. By late spring, water lily leaves cover some of the smaller coastal plain ponds, providing tiny island refuges for insects and amphibians. By midsummer, the plant, whose rhizomous roots anchor it into the substrate below, produces a white multipetaled flower that also floats on the water. The tranquillity and beauty of a pond crowded with blooming lilies is a sight unrivaled on Long Island.

Pondweeds (Potamogeton) are the largest family of truly aquatic plants found in North America. Pondweeds are perennials and, like water lilies, they anchor their roots in the pond's substrate and have floating leaves, but they also produce many underwater leaves. The floating and underwater leaves show a dichotomy in that the underwater leaves are usually much narrower than the floaters. The dense underwater growth of pondweeds is an important refuge and source of food for many of the pond's creatures. Most pondweeds have a spikelike flower that produces many small seeds, but they also reproduce vegetatively, from tubers in the mud that often break apart and become new plants.

Unlike water lilies and pondweeds, the duckweeds (Lemnaceae spp.) are a family of plants, represented by several species on Long Island, that completely float, roots and all. Duckweeds are the smallest flowering and seed-producing plants on Long Island and look like nothing more than tiny pieces of green confetti sprinkled across the water. They have no leaves; instead, the plant body is a specialized disc-shaped stem that is dense with chlorophyll and functions as a photosynthetic leaf. From this floating structure, that is no more than an eighth of an inch across, there often hangs short slender rootlets, the number varying among the different species. You can forget about seeing this plant in bloom. The flowers are minute, and most years the perennial plants do not produce any blooms at all. They more commonly employ vegetative reproduction methods, producing new plants by lateral branching. In autumn, the new branches fall to the pond's bottom, where they ride out the winter until spring, when they rise to the surface and grow.

Besides floating aquatic plants, there are also emergents vying for space in the coastal plain ponds. Emergents are plants that grow "with their feet in the water." They have their root systems in the pond's sandy substrate, while most of the leaves and flowering parts remain above the water. One of the most beautiful emergents found at the Calverton Ponds are the yellow-eyed grasses, all members of the family Xyridaceae. Superficially they all resemble grasses, with their bladelike leaves rising one or two feet out of the water. In midsummer, tiny bright-yellow flowers appear on top of a leafless stalk. These develop into fruit capsules that resemble tiny dried pineapples and persist throughout the winter until the movement of ice on the pond's surface snips them. Calverton's Fox Pond has good numbers of yellow-eyed grasses growing in its shallow margins. The plants bloom in midsummer, at which time the watery pond seems transformed into a flowering prairie.

Another group of emergents found in the coastal plain ponds are the bladderworts, members of the family *Lentibulariaceae*. There are several species of them on Long Island, and all have yellow flowers except for the purple bladderwort (*Utricularia purpurea*). Bladderworts are carnivorous plants that capture small animals, mostly minute crustaceans, to supplement their nitrogen uptake, and their curious name is descriptive of their unorthodox feeding mechanism. They have underwater leaves adorned with tiny chambers, or "bladders," with small trapdoors. Small trigger hairs surrounding each "door" respond to the movement of tiny organisms, causing the door to open. Simultaneously, the bladder inflates, sucking in water and, hopefully, the organisms. The door shuts and enzymatic activity digests the unfortunate creatures. One species, swollen bladderwort (*Utricularia inflata*), has inflated leaf stalks that resemble tiny cigars. The underwater stems surround the plant's central stalk in a whorl and serve to hold the plant in place.

The Calverton Ponds are home to a few very rare species of aquatic plants. One globally endangered plant found there is the quill-leaved arrowhead (*Sagittaria teres*). Arrowheads are a large group of perennial emer-

gents, with several common species growing on Long Island. Most of them have distinctive leaves shaped like an Indian arrowhead and produce a flower stalk with three-petaled white blossoms. They grow from submerged starchy tubers that were an important food for Native Americans and continue to be so for native animals. Muskrats are particularly fond of them. The quill-leaved arrowhead is atypical in that its leaves do not have the distinctive arrowhead shape but are linear blades. This is a very rare arrowhead known only from a small number of coastal plain ponds along the Eastern Seaboard.

As the summer waxes, the water table usually drops and the coastal plain ponds shrink. The process is gradual, eventually exposing a wide margin of wet pond substrate. Annual plants, whose seeds may lie dormant for years during wet periods when the exposed pond margins do not appear, quickly colonize the area. Many of the annuals that fill this niche are quite rare: at the Calverton Ponds these include the globally endangered drowned horn-rush (*Rhynchospora inundata*) and the short-beaked rush (*Psilocarya nitens*). Rushes are herbaceous plants, usually with grasslike leaves growing from a basal tuft and inconspicuous green or brown flowers. On Long Island, rushes exist in habitats ranging from salt marshes to fields, but the two aforementioned species grow only on the coastal plain ponds' margins.

None of the midsummer annuals that grow luxuriously on the pond margins are large and showy, most being small, grasslike, and individually inconspicuous. They grow, however, in bands segregated by species, and their unique coloring often creates understated

yet stunning displays. One common colonist is the golden hedge-hyssop (*Gratiola aurea*). It is a tiny plant, usually growing no more than a few inches high, but its leaves are emerald green and its yellow flowers are as golden as the sun.

An array of wildlife complements the great diversity of plant life in the coastal plain pond community, including both permanent inhabitants and occasional visitors. The twilight hours will often find deer at the pond margins dining on succulent aquatic vegetation. During migratory periods, good numbers of waterfowl pass through. Wading birds such as great blue herons (*Ardea herodias*) and great egrets visit the ponds to do a little fishing, while raccoons and opossums frequent the ponds in search of frogs or fish. The larger ponds maintain populations of native fish, but it is at the smaller ponds that usually dry out each year where we find some of the more unusual creatures.

During an early morning visit to the ponds, there is a good chance you will see the motionless mirror-like surface of the water broken by the sinuous wake of the northern water snake (*Nerodia sipedon*). Water snakes are common throughout the pine barrens: they patrol the water and surrounding shore both day and night in search of frogs, fish, small mammals, and other prey. Northern water snakes can grow to be four feet long, but most specimens are half that size. They are extremely variable in their markings, usually being reddish brown to black with a lighter belly and alternating dark blotches along their backs. The older they get, the darker the overall pattern becomes. Most Long Island specimens are very dark. Although there are no poisonous snakes on

Long Island, many people mistake water snakes for poisonous water moccasins (Agkistrodon piscivorus) and kill them. (The timber rattlesnake (Crotalus horridus) is the only poisonous snake recorded on Long Island, but the last individual was spotted in 1912.) Unfortunately, snakes, especially poisonous species, have been the object of fear and persecution throughout human history. Most snakes are harmless unless you torment or try to capture one. Furthermore, they are an important part of the environment and their presence is an indication of a healthy natural community. The disappearance of snakes from an area is a clear sign of some sort of disturbance to that habitat.

Ribbon snakes (Thamnophis sauritus) are another common semiaquatic species that inhabits the pond margins. While water snakes are thick, large, and robust, ribbon snakes are small and slender, almost pencil thin. They usually get no longer than one and a half to two feet, and one-third of this length is tail. Since a snake looks like it is only tail, I should note that the tail is the region posterior to the cloaca. The cloaca is the common opening for digestive, urinary, and reproductive functions in all vertebrates except, for the most part, mammals. Ribbon snakes are dark with three bright stripes, usually yellow, running the length of the animal. Like water snakes, ribbon snakes are agile swimmers that seem to defy gravity by effortlessly gliding across water.

Tiger salamanders (Ambystoma tigrinum) are the largest salamanders on Long Island, with most specimens reaching a length of about eight inches. They are members of the mole family of salamanders, and they spend most of

the year underground in search of worms and other insects. Their dorsal side is dark black or brown and they are covered with irregular light olive to yellow spots. Tiger salamanders are listed as a state endangered species and in New York breed only on Long Island; they are found in selected sites in Nassau County and on the South Fork, but their numbers are greatest in the coastal plain ponds of the pine barrens. They especially favor the temporary ponds as breeding pools because of their lack of predators such as fish. Even though tiger salamanders are cold-blooded creatures, they begin their breeding cycle in late winter when many ponds still have a cover of ice. The males emerge first from their sandy burrows and enter the ponds, usually in February but some years as early as January. The females enter the ponds shortly thereafter, and an elaborate courtship dance follows between the two. Fertilization in tiger salamanders is internal, but the male has no copulatory organ. Instead, he deposits a packet of sperm called a spermatophore on the pond's bottom; this enters the female's cloaca when she lowers herself on it. Like frogs, tiger salamanders lay their eggs in a protective gelatinous mass that hatches in about three to four weeks. The gilled young metamorphose into adults by the end of the summer, when they leave the pond to begin their subterranean existence.

During a summertime visit to the coastal plain ponds, it would be hard to miss the ubiquitous presence of flying insects. There are annoying pests, like mosquitoes and biting flies, but to keep them in check there are also dragon- and damselflies. Dragon- and damselflies are members of the order Odonata, an ancient group of insects dating back in the fossil record more than three hundred

million years. They have long slender bodies and four powerful wings. Generally dragonflies hold their wings flat and horizontally to the side, while damselflies hold theirs to the rear, vertically. They are both voracious predators of other flying insects and can efficiently clear the sky of a swarm of biting pests in minutes. They deposit their eggs in the water where the young, called naiads, exist as predators until leaving the pond to metamorphose into the adult form. The barrens bluet (Enallagma recurvatum) is an endangered species of damselfly known only from Long Island's coastal plain ponds and coastal plain ponds in Cape Cod and New Jersey.

The coastal plain ponds are a unique relic of our geological past that provide cradles of diversity in the otherwise homogenous pine barrens. Their fragile nature makes them susceptible to small changes in the environment, both natural and otherwise. Their existence is precariously linked to human activities, such as overuse and pollution of groundwater supplies. For this reason, they stand as a barometer that can indicate even subtle changes in the overall environmental health of Long Island. Their beauty and importance should not be overlooked.

In the wake of melting glaciers, Long Island's landscape became riddled with streams and rivers and pockmarked with kettle ponds and swampy depressions. Many of the latter lacked good drainage and had little surface inflow or outflow: silt and debris cannot exit and oxygen and food cannot enter. Over long periods of time their bottoms slowly filled with plant debris. Simultaneously, plant growth in the water expanded until a floating vegetative mat covered

Fragrant water lily
(*Nymphaea odorata*) is one of
the most common aquatic
plants of Long Island's coastal
plain ponds. It frequently
grows so densely that the lily
pads hide the pond's surface.

A small pond in Sears Bellows
Pond County Park is covered
by the blossoms of fragrant
water lily in June. The pine
barrens in this vicinity is dotted with many small ponds,
contributing to the region's
beauty and the diversity of its
flora and fauna.

Sunset light illuminates the tranquil waters of Grassy Pond, a coastal plain pond in Peconic River County Park.

Opposite:
Sandy Stream Pond is one of Long Island's finest examples of a coastal plain pond.

The golden blossoms of yellow-
eyed grasses *(Xyridaceae spp.)*
cover the shallow margins of
Fox Pond by midsummer.

Opposite:
**The yellow flowers of bladder-
worts** *(Utricularia spp.)* stand
out in the dark water of a Long
Island bog.

The northern pitcher plant
(Sarracenia purpurea) is an uncommon carnivorous plant that grows in a handful of bogs on Long Island. Bogs are nutrient poor, and pitcher plants have developed a strategy of extracting necessary nutrients, primarily nitrogen, from animal tissue, by capturing and digesting insects.

the water's surface and emergents grew out from the water's edge. The most characteristic plant of the vegetative mat is sphagnum moss (Sphagnum spp.—the sphagnum genus contains a number of species that are rather difficult to distinguish). Special cells in the sphagnum's leaves are able to absorb up to sixteen times their weight in water, making these plants well suited for life on a waterlogged surface. Sphagnum is what makes up the familiar peat moss sold in garden shops. The water trapped under the sphagnum mat is stagnant and oxygen depleted and remains cool due to the insulating effects of the sphagnum above. These conditions are not conducive to the growth of decomposing organisms, so organic debris is only partially broken down. Material accumulates as peat on the bottom, and this releases humic acid, further intensifing the harsh conditions. Eventually the pond or swamp becomes choked with peat and a bog is formed. The lack of oxygen, a highly acid environment, and a lack of nutrients (which are tied up in only partially decomposed organic materials) are the limiting factors that exclude all but highly adapted species from living here.

The sterility of a bog's peat layers is legendary. Timber from fallen trees has been removed from bogs in excellent condition after being submersed for hundreds of years. Bogs also have been known to preserve the remains of animals centuries old. Scientists have been able to reconstruct weather conditions and vegetative cover on Long Island since the last period of glaciation by looking at pollen preserved in peat layers. The succession of dominant plant species over time indicates that Long Island's postglacial climate has progressed from cool/dry to warm

to cool/humid. The period of maximum warming, called the hypsithermal interval, occurred about seven to four thousand years ago.

The spongy wet surface of a bog offers plenty of water but little in the way of nutrients to plants. Usable nitrogen is especially low due to the lack of decomposing bacteria, and carnivorous plants that extract nitrogen from insects are well suited for life here. The northern pitcher plant (Sarracenia purpurea) is the most conspicuous of these. Its insect-catching ability lies within the specialized rosette of leaves at its base. The leaves— fleshy, tube-shaped structures with a thick ruffled lip—act as pitchers to collect rainwater. Glands on the lip secrete a nectar that attracts insects, usually flies. An insect that enters the "pitcher" becomes trapped by short, bristly hairs that point downward and drowns in the rainwater: nutrients released by its decomposition are absorbed by the plant. In midsummer, pitcher plants produce a single red flower on a leafless stalk. The plant's large petals drop quickly, but the umbrellalike style sometimes lingers through winter.

You may notice little tufts of reddish vegetation growing about the bog that glisten as if covered by morning dew even during the middle of the driest day. These are sundews, another carnivorous inhabitant of the bog, of which three species exist on Long Island. The round-leaved sundew (Drosera rotundifolia) and the spatulate-leaved sundew (Drosera intermedia) are most common, with the thread-leaved sundew (Drosera filiformis) being the rarest (you can see them at Hither Hills State Park in East Hampton). Each species is named for the distinctive shape of its leaves. The first two bear small white flowers on a leafless flower stalk; the flowers of the last are purple. Sundews are small plants, only a few inches high, with leaves growing from a basal rosette; these are covered with glandular hairs that secrete a sweet but sticky substance (the "dew") that attracts and then traps small insects. The digested insects supplement the plant's root-derived nutrients, which, of course, are poor in a bog.

The aforementioned bog plants are unusual and probably unfamiliar to most people. There is one plant, however, that is familiar to all. American cranberry (Vaccinium macrocarpon) is a small, evergreen member of the heath family with a trailing growth habit, which grows intertwined with the bog's sphagnum, reaching a maximum height of eight inches. The flowers have four white (or sometimes pink) petals that curve backward while the stamens and anthers join into a cone projecting forward. By autumn, the tasty red berries are ready to pick. These may linger throughout winter into the following spring, and I have found that berries harvested long after autumn are the sweetest. The closely related wren's egg cranberry (Vaccinium oxycoccos) also grows on Long Island and differs from American cranberry in that its leaves are smaller, with rolled edges and white beneath.

The cranberry is host plant to the larva of a small butterfly called the bog copper (Epidemia epixanthe). Even though cranberries are locally abundant in appropriate habitat on Long Island, bog coppers are rare. They have only one brood per season, with the adults usually flying in July; no more than an inch across, they look more like moths as they feebly flit about the bog. Bog coppers characteristically exist in small colonies, with some having only

fifty to one hundred individuals, and this, more than anything else, might account for their scarcity. Small isolated colonies are subject to easy eradication by human disturbance or pathogens.

The succession from pond to bog is a slow one that eventually changes the entire plant community in an area. During the process, the edges of the bog reach a point where they can sustain the growth of larger woody shrubs. Leatherleaf (Chamaedaphne calyculata), a member of the heath family with small leathery leaves, is one such shrub. In early summer it has tiny white bell-shaped flowers that dangle from its stems. Leatherleaf grows at the edge of still waters and, along with sphagnum moss, is responsible for forming the floating vegetative mats that eventually create a bog. Once the vegetative mat along the edge of a pond stabilizes and becomes thick with peat, other shrubs can begin to colonize the newly formed spongy turf.

Sweet gale (Myrica gale) is an evergreen shrub that reaches a height of six feet. It has small nonleathery wedge-shaped leaves with toothed tips and distinctive resin dots that help identify the plant. Sweet gale is a close relative of bayberry (Myrica pensylvanica), a common shrub along Long Island's shorelines, and, like bayberry, sweet gale has aromatic foliage once used to flavor foods and scent clothing. Labrador tea (Ledum groenlandicum) is another low-growing shrub common in bogs. It has leathery evergreen leaves with rolled edges. The undersides of the leaves are thick with white or rust-colored hairs that resemble fur. Like sweet gale's, Labrador tea leaves are aromatic and were used by Colonial settlers to make tea. In June, tiny white flowers in terminal clusters appear along the stems,

adding a spot of brightness to the green monotony of the bog.

There are a number of attractive wildflowers that bloom in bogs. Orchids are the largest family of flowering plants in the world, with more than twenty thousand species worldwide, and there are at least twenty found on Long Island today, with historical records for several others now extirpated. Many of these species thrive along the margins of bogs, where other flowering plants would surely fail. The white-fringed orchid (Habernaria blephariglottis) has leaves that resemble blades of grass, which are easy to overlook in spring. By June or July, however, you would have to be blind to miss this exotic plant: on top of a single flower stalk are arranged clusters of white flowers with fringed lip petals. All orchids' blossoms have three petals, with the bottom petal differentiated into a complex lip. Many orchid lips have backward-projecting spurs and the white-fringed orchid is no exception. They are spectacular plants that can reach two feet high with a flower cluster six inches high and three inches in diameter. The white-fringed orchid's exotic beauty perfectly complements the mysterious nature of the bogs where they live.

Within the pine barrens there are ponds and swamps whose outer margins have become stable bogs, while their innermost parts are still open water. A superb example of this phenomenon, called Maple Swamp after the lush growth of red maples (Acer rubrum) bordering the open water, can be found in a region of the pine barrens south of Riverhead. (Red maples take their common name because in all seasons some part of the tree is red, but they are

A red maple *(Acer rubrum)* seed lays on a bed of sphagnum moss *(Sphagnum spp.)* at Red Maple Swamp.

also called swamp maple, which may be more fitting since these trees rarely grow where water is absent.) Maple Swamp has been slowly filling with organic debris from the edges inward; hundreds of years from now there will be no open water, just mats of sphagnum and bog-loving plants.

For now, however, this is one of the most beautiful spots in the pine barrens. Approaching by foot, you can begin to sense the transition between the dry pine barrens and the swamp community as you descend ever so slightly in elevation. When you reach the maples,

the air is cooler, thanks to the influence of the water, and bird life is more diverse. The buzzing call of the pine barrens' prairie warblers are replaced with the bright peals of the swamp's redstarts *(Setophaga ruticilla).* Redstarts are colorful warblers that erratically flutter through the trees in pursuit of insects, looking more like butterflies than birds.

Bogs not colonized by red maples often become populated by Atlantic white cedars. Atlantic white cedar *(Chamaecyparis thyoides)* is a cone-bearing evergreen tree of the eastern coastal plain always found in or near water and never far from the coast. They do not have distinct needles or typical cones like their cone-bearing relatives, the pitch pines. Instead, their flat, overlapping blue-green leaves are one-sixteenth to one-eighth-inch wide, appearing more like green twigs than evergreen leaves or needles. With their scaly surface, they resemble reptile limbs. The cones are as peculiar as the leaves, being spherical and tiny, about a quarter-inch in diameter. The new cones are bluish-purple with a powdery bloom and have six cone scales culminating in a pointy tip. As they grow, they turn reddish brown, beginning to look more like evergreen cones. They mature in only one season, with each cone scale usually yielding two winged seeds capable of traveling miles on the wind. White cedars have reddish-brown bark that sloughs off in narrow vertical strips like the shreddings of a peeled carrot. The trees may not sound that attractive, but with all their odd characteristics, they somehow form one of the most beautiful natural communities on Long Island.

Since the cedars grow in wet bogs, you would not think that fire is important in their life history,

but it is. After a fire runs through a bog, the cleared burned peat is the perfect starting medium for cedar seedlings. They grow rapidly and quickly outcompete other colonizing vegetation. This explains why most cedar grooves consist of uniform height trees: they were all "born" the same season. The trees with their dense pointed crowns often grow close together, monopolizing the available open space. The overall effect is dark and oppressive, and when walking among the trees you get a definite feeling of being confined by their engulfing presence.

Before the European settlers arrived on Long Island, the pine barrens burned regularly and had numerous bogs; hence there were many white cedar swamps. Today only a fraction remains. Sizable groves remain in Cranberry Bog Preserve and in Flanders County Park, but other groves consist of only a handful of trees. Early coastal settlers soon discovered that cedar was resistant to rotting and therefore valuable for ship-building, shingles, posts, wooden utensils, and so forth. Even logs from ancient trees were mined from bogs and used for lumber, attesting to the value placed on white cedar wood. Over-harvesting, direct habitat destruction, and fire suppression are factors that worked to severely reduce the number of cedar groves on Long Island.

Most of Long Island's unusual and rare plant communities have unusual and rare animal life associated with them, and cedar groves are no exception. The blue-green leaves of white cedar are the host vegetation for the Hessel's hairstreak *(Mitoura hesseli).* Hessel's hairstreaks are small butterflies, about one inch across.

The males have dark brown wings above, while females are more reddish brown. When they alight, their folded wings show their colorful undersides: a rich metallic-looking green with a bluish sheen in places. They have two white hind-wing bands bordered with brown and other assorted white-and-brown markings. The hind wings also have two narrow hair-like projections, hence the name "hairstreak."

The Hessel's hairstreak and olive hairstreak *(Mitoura gryneus)* are two very closely related species. Their kinship is such that the two are almost exactly identical in appearance and very difficult to distinguish from one another. Hessel's hairstreak, however, confines itself to the white cedar as a host plant; the olive hairstreak's larva feed on red cedar *(Juniperus virginiana)*. While white cedar has restricted habitat demands, the red cedar occurs everywhere and is a widespread and efficient colonizer of old fields; consequently, it is very abundant. The two species probably represent an example of clado-genesis. Cladogenesis is an evolutionary mechanism responsible for biological diversity: it consists of the branching or budding of one or more new species from an existing one. Hessel's hair-streak is much rarer than the olive hairstreak because its required host plants became rare; indeed, it has gone unrecorded on Long Island for several years, even though there remain cedar groves large enough to support a popula-tion. Interestingly, despite good numbers of red cedars throughout the island, the olive hairstreak is rare as well. Perhaps these two sister species have other more subtle, and yet unrecognized, liv-ing requirements that are not being met in the 1990s.

White-fringed orchids *(Habernaria blephariglottis)* grow near a bracken fern *(Pteridium aquilinum)* in a bog in Connetquot River State Park.

A highbush blueberry
(*Vaccinium corymbosum*) on
Sandy Pond displays red twigs
in early winter. At this point in
the year, many ponds are near
full, having recovered from
summer losses.

Opposite:
A large Atlantic white cedar
(*Chamaecyparis thyoides*) at
the edge of Penny Pond in
Flanders County Park.

Backlit royal ferns (*Osmunda regalis*) stand out against a backdrop of cranberries and grasses in a cranberry bog in Napeague State Park.

Bushy stands of leatherleaf (*Chamaedaphne calyculata*) grow on the sphagnum mats that ring this small coastal plain pond. Colonization by leatherleaf and sphagnum moss is the first step in transforming the sphagnum bog into more permanent and drier land.

Red Maple Swamp becomes choked
with colorful floating leaves during
autumn.

Opposite:
Sunrise over a boggy area in Cranberry
Bog County Park near Riverhead. This
area supports an amazing diversity of
life, including many rare and endangered
species of plants and animals. Visible in
the distance are Atlantic white cedars,
now quite rare on Long Island.

CHAPTER 8

RIVERS AND STREAMS

The role of glaciers in sculpting Long Island's present form cannot be stressed enough. Their tools were water and till, the till being the sculptor's medium and water the chisel. The glacier's chisel sculpted the till into moraines and outwash plains. The sculptor finished this work by etching dendritic patterns across the countenance of its piece. These are Long Island's rivers and streams.

Many of Long Island's natural features are atypical, and its rivers and streams are no exception. On the mainland, the majority of rivers and streams serve as runoff channels from high ground over rock substrate where little seepage occurs. In contrast, Long Island's waterways represent superficial manifestations of groundwater through porous layers of gravel and sand. Long Island's streams are characteristically still and slow moving, more like a pond with a long sinuous shape than the familiar fast-flowing river.

The slow movement of the streams reflects the flow of groundwater within the island's substrate. Long Island literally floats on water. The deposits laid down by glaciers over hundreds of thousands of years left stratified layers of varying bands of material, from dense clay to coarse gravel and everything in-between. Where clay sits below a stratum of unconsolidated sand and gravel, any water percolating through that stratum eventually becomes stalled at the clay layer that is relatively impervious to water. In this way, vast pools of water have accumulated underground in sand and gravel layers called aquifers. Estimates indicate that Long Island's aquifers, some of which are arranged on top of each other separated by bands of nonporous clay, hold more than sixty trillion gallons of fresh water.

The oldest of the island's aquifers are also the deepest and date back to the Cretaceous period more than sixty-five million years ago. Here, fossil water as old as the dinosaurs exists with no inflow or outflow. Rainwater seeping through the ground only recharges the uppermost aquifers: this is why it is important to maintain open areas such as the pine barrens. Long Islanders get their drinking water from the aquifers. The demand for water has grown enormously, and, while we pump more water out, development above hinders the flow of rainwater back into the aquifers. Water is also lost to the sea by way of our sewer systems. Long Island's aquifers are in contact with the sea under the water's surface, and normally the abundant fresh water seeps slowly into the sea; now, however, salt water seeps into the aquifers replacing the fresh water we have removed, and some drink-

ing water wells on Long Island have even become tainted in this way. To satisfy the need for more water, we have drilled wells deeper into the fossil water reserves, but these are, alas, finite. The result of development and population growth is that Long Island's streams and rivers have been depleted of their life-giving fluid. Walt Whitman called Long Island an "isle of sweet brooks of drinking-water," but later in life he acknowledged that the numerous brooks he once knew had vanished. Today, Long Island's flowing surface water is a fraction of what it once was.

Because Long Island is not a very large landmass, freshwater runoff to the sea does not have the opportunity to gather into large rivers. The Peconic is the longest river on Long Island, and it is only about twelve miles long. The streams and rivers on Long Island essentially follow three main drainage patterns. In Brooklyn, Queens, and Nassau counties, the Harbor Hill Moraine divides the watersheds into north and south parcels. Everything north of the moraine flows to the sound, while everything south heads toward the Atlantic. The Ronkonkoma Moraine lies south of the Harbor Hill Moraine, but does not interfere with the flow of water, which crosses through the numerous breaks formed by ancient glacial meltwaters. In Suffolk County, however, the Ronkonkoma Moraine is more formidable, and consequently a west to east watershed exists between the moraines, emptying into the Great Peconic Bay. The Peconic River supplies the drainage here and is the only river flowing laterally across the island.

Long Island has four major rivers, the Peconic, the Carmans, the Connetquot, and the Nissequogue. Despite their relatively short lengths, all have extremely

wide mouths carved out by rising postglacial seas. The mouths of Long Island's rivers are therefore under the influence of the ocean tides rising and falling in daily rhythm; the resulting brackish mixture of fresh water and salt water is characteristic of an estuary.

The Peconic River's headwaters can be found among a group of coastal plain ponds in Peconic River County Park, to the east of Brookhaven National Laboratory. An unorganized swampy seepage of water from the ponds consolidates into a small stream around Manorville. Like all of Long Island's rivers, the Peconic experienced alterations at the hands of settlers. Dams to provide power for various industries, from gristmills to iron forges, created small ponds. Settlers also lowered the level of rivers by draining water for irrigation. Despite changes like this, the Peconic remains Long Island's most wild river.

The section of river around Manorville is especially beautiful and probably best seen by canoe. Here the river is narrow and wild, with the branches of gently overhanging trees creating a tunnel. The area is full of birds and other critters. I have seen ruby-throated hummingbirds (*Archilochus colubris*) in this area during the summer on more than one occasion, although I have never found evidence of nesting. Hummingbirds are uncommon and sporadic nesters on Long Island, with the South Fork being the most likely place to find breeders. Perhaps the abundance of jewelweed (*Impatiens capensis*) that grows along the river, a favorite source of nectar for them, is the area's attraction. Jewelweed is a succulent wildflower growing one to

A jewelweed (*Impatiens capensis*) blossom growing along the Peconic River shines with early morning dew.

The brilliant red autumn leaves of black huckleberry (*Gaylussacia baccata*) brighten the shoreline of Grassy Pond in Peconic River County Park. This and several other coastal plain ponds in the area form the headwaters of Long Island's longest river.

three feet high in moist, shaded soils. The golden-orange blossoms dangle from the plant like Christmas ornaments on short dainty stems. The flower's odd shape—a cone with a little spur at the closed end, opening out into three petals—has evolved so that hummingbirds can pollinate it, although insects remain the primary pollinators. The juice from the stem can relieve the itch from poison ivy or insect bites and has a fungicidal component as well.

The wider, pondlike areas along the Peconic River are good spots to see waterfowl and other birds. Some of these areas become choked with floating vegetation by

late summer. An interesting plant common among the aquatic plants is dodder (*Cuscuta gronovii*). Dodder is a climbing vine that begins its life as a germinating seed in the moist soil bordering the river, but shortly thereafter the vine takes on the lifestyle of a parasite relying on the life processes of a host plant to sustain its growth. The vines twist around other nearby plants and literally suck the life out of them. Lacking chlorophyll, their leaves are nothing more than vestigial scales and their stems are colored orange. (Chlorophyll, the substance necessary for photosynthesis, colors plants green; when it is absent, a plant's color is influenced by other compounds. We see this every autumn, when green plants stop producing chlorophyll and their leaves take on the color of the dominate compound within them.) Dodder vines obtain nutrients by invading their hosts with small modified roots called haustorium. The haustorium enters the host's vascular tissues, where it absorbs water and nutrients. In some years dodder is rampant along the river. Severe dodder infestations look like tomato sauce–soaked spaghetti thrown across the host plants.

Sweezy Pond in Cranberry Bog County Park in Riverhead, created by damming the Little Peconic River, a tributary of the Peconic, is a beautiful, still body of water covered with mats of water lilies in summer. The diversity of life found within the pond is outstanding. Fifteen species of fish have been recorded, as well as six species of turtles, including musk turtles (*Sternotherus oderatus*) and mud turtles (*Kinosternon subrubrum*), two rare reptiles on Long Island. The pond is immediately surrounded by red maples, sour gums, and other plants adapted to life in wet environments. One of the most interesting is swamp honeysuckle

(*Rhododendron viscosum*), so named because of its sticky blossom's strong, perfumelike odor. Swamp honeysuckle, by the way, is not a true honeysuckle (*Lonicera spp.*) but actually a member of the heath family, like so many other pine barrens plants. It grows in wet areas, reaching a height of three to nine feet, and blooms during June and July.

Long Island's next largest river after the Peconic is the Carmans, which is about ten miles long. The Carmans River begins as a small spring near Route 25 in Middle Island. From here, it flows southward, first passing through Cathedral Pines County Park and then under the Long Island Expressway, where it enters South Haven County Park. South of Sunrise Highway it passes through Wertheim National Wildlife Refuge and then empties into Bellport Bay and the Great South Bay. At its beginnings, the Carmans is a small stream, only widening appreciably around Yaphank, where several dams have formed large lakes. South of the expressway through the northern part of South Haven County Park the river is most attractive. It passes through dense woodlands bordered by hardwood trees and shrubs that are especially beautiful when they show their autumn colors.

One of the showiest autumn trees along the Carmens River is the sour gum (*Nyssa sylvatica*). This deciduous tree grows in wetlands across Long Island, reaching a height of forty to sixty feet with a straight trunk and branches that grow perpendicular from the trunk and horizontal to the ground. Deep grooves running both vertically and horizontally in the tree's bark create a checkerboard pattern. It is one of the first hardwoods to show its autumn colors; by mid-September, its leathery

Sour gum trees (*Nyssa sylvatica*) growing along the Carmans River.

White pine (*Pinus albus*) can also be found along the Carmans River in South Haven County Park. This stand was planted.

Opposite:
Morning mist rising from the Peconic River at sunrise. The Peconic is Long Island's longest river and the only one that flows horizontally across the island, from west to east. The river begins as the outflow from a region of coastal plain ponds in Peconic River County Park and takes a shallow, slow moving course on its way to the Peconic Bay in Riverhead. The Peconic abounds with wildlife and wildflowers while passing through some of Long Island's most pristine and ecologically important regions and is probably best enjoyed by canoe.

The northern pintail duck *(Anas acuta)* is a North American species that is commonly found on Long Island during the autumn and winter. They are particularly fond of still bodies of water like the mill pond on the Connetquot River in Connetquot River State Park, where this male was photographed.

The yellow-crested orchid *(Habenaria cristata)* is a rare plant that grows in several widely scattered locations on Long Island. This specimen was blossoming early in July along the upper Connetquot River.

leaves are a rich cranberry red color: when backlit in morning light, the tree appears to be on fire. Sour gums produce a small black fruit that humans find bitter tasting but wildlife seem to relish.

The Connetquot River begins just south of the Ronkonkoma Moraine in Lakeland County Park as a spring seepage in a swampy area. This is a beautiful area with a boardwalk trail that winds through the swamp and around a small pond. From here the river flows south through Connetquot River State Park. At this point the Connetquot is a cool and clear trout stream passing through a fine example of pine barrens vegetation. To the west of the river near Bunces Bridge there is Long Island's only known population of pyxie moss *(Pyxidanthera barbulata)*. This is a creeping plant that grows only an inch or two high. In spring it has tiny bell-shaped pink flowers, making it easier to find than when not in bloom, as it resembles a patch of moss. Once again, we are here observing a southern species at what is probably its northernmost distribution. Further south, the wetlands along the river are mostly red maple swamps with a ground cover of emerald green sphagnum and a lush growth of cinnamon ferns *(Osmunda cinnamomea)*. Netted chain fern *(Woodwardia areolata)*, a coastal plain species and one of Long Island's most beautiful ferns, is also found in this area. Netted chain fern grows from a creeping underground rootstock and has glossy, bright green leaves that have a translucent quality. At the southern end of the park, the river flows into a fifteen-acre millpond that attracts large numbers of migrating waterfowl. This is a good spot for common merganser *(Mergus merganser)*, hooded merganser *(Lophodytes cuculatus)*, and redheads *(Aythya americana)*,

three uncommon ducks on Long Island. South of Sunrise Highway, the river widens and becomes an estuary, under the influence of the tides. The river empties into Nicholl Bay, a cove in the Great South Bay.

The Nissequogue River is the only Long Island river that begins in the Ronkonkoma Moraine and flows north, crossing the Harbor Hill Moraine and then emptying into the Long Island Sound. About nine miles long, it begins as a series of small springs and tributaries near the Suffolk County Center in Hauppauge. Near its source, it flows into Mill Pond, in Blydenburgh County Park. Mill Pond is the second largest lake on Long Island and, as its name suggests, was the site of a gristmill. From there, the river winds through Caleb Smith State Park, where it becomes a swiftly moving trout stream. Brook trout *(Salvelinus fontinalis)* are native to its waters, but the state also stocks the river with brown trout *(Salmo trutta)* and rainbow trout *(Salmo gairdneri)*. Many people consider this section of the river to be the most beautiful waterway on the island. The surrounding forest is lush, the water runs clear, and the summer woods ring with the song of the Carolina wren *(Thryothorus ludovicianus)* and the wood thrush *(Hylocichla mustelina)*. A more ideal setting would be hard to imagine. The woods bordering the river are a good place to see the downy rattlesnake plantain *(Goodyera pubescens)*, a rare orchid on Long Island. Its attractive leaves, about two to three inches long, grow from a basal rosette and are dark green with a network of white veins forming a checkerboard pattern. Its small white flowers grow atop a leafless hairy stalk.

After crossing Route 25, the Nissequogue begins to mix with salt water. The river widens and the vegetation slowly changes from cattails to salt marsh cord-grass. Near its mouth the river comes and goes with the tides, revealing vast mud flats when the tide is low. The mud flats with their tidal channels are good places to look for waders and shorebirds. Near the mouth of the river, to the west, are the impressive seventy-five-foot-high Kings Park Bluffs. On the way to the sound, the Nissequogue finally passes between two huge sand spits; the eastern spit, called Short Beach, has New York's largest colony of breeding least terns (*Sterna antillarum)*, and although the colony is off-limits, the terns are easily seen fishing in the Nissequogue and Long Island Sound.

Hundreds of streams on Long Island have disappeared under bricks and concrete in the past half-century. Shu Swamp Preserve in Mill Neck is an excellent example of a freshwater spring and stream complex once very common on Long Island's North Shore. The moist woodlands are dominated by tulip trees. The grove here is one of the best preserved on Long Island, with trees nearly one hundred feet tall. The trees support large numbers of woodland birds; this is one of the surest places on the island to see red-bellied woodpeckers.

The swamp attracts many species of water-loving birds. Snowy egrets and green-backed herons commonly use the swamp as a fishing hole, and great blue heron sometimes make an appearance as well. Interesting breeding birds recorded here have included the least bittern (*Ixobrychus exilis)*, a small secretive heron of marshes and swamps, and the Louisiana waterthrush (*Seiurus motacilla)*, which, as its name sug-

A white-tailed deer (*Odocoileus virginianus*) swims across the Connetquot River early one morning.

gests, normally has a more southern distribution. Other sporadic breeders include the yellow-throated vireo (Vireo flavifrons), wood duck (Aix sponsa), red-shouldered hawk (Buteo lineatus), and broad-winged hawk (Buteo platypterus).

There are numbers of interesting water-loving shrubs found here. Winterberry holly (Ilex decidua) grows in abundance on one side of the swamp. Winterberry is closely related to the American holly of Long Island's maritime forests, yet significant differences exist. A small (normally about ten feet tall) deciduous shrub, it is rather nondescript in leaf, unlike the showy evergreen American holly. The plant's true beauty becomes evident in winter, when small, bright red berries decorate its gray stems. The contrast of the berries against a snow-covered swamp is striking. Many birds and mammals look to the fruit of winterberry as an important supplement to their winter diet.

Poison sumac (Toxicodendron vernix) is also a shrubby attractive plant, but don't pick a bouquet of sumac berries for your vase. Poison sumac is one of the most toxic plants in North America, and many people have a reaction immediately after touching it. Like its relative poison ivy, poison sumac bears attractive white berries and, although harmful to humans, apparently has no ill effect on birds and small mammals.

There are numerous small mammals at Shu Swamp, including muskrats and red fox. One rainy day in August of 1987, I was fortunate enough to find a longtail weasel (Mustela frenata) and her young at the stump of a rotting tulip tree. These slender, wiry animals about a foot long with short legs, a long tail, and long neck are voracious carnivores able to take prey much larger than themselves. They are probably more common on Long Island than many people believe, but their preference to live in swampy habitats and secretive nature make them hard to detect.

Creeks and streams also occur in the pine barrens, where they develop boglike characteristics. In Massapequa Preserve on the South Shore, a small creek runs through the only remaining example of the pine barrens in Nassau County. Parts of the creek here are shallow, broad, and still; consequently, boggy margins have developed with the expected plants of a pine barrens bog, including leatherleaf, swamp honeysuckle, and highbush blueberry, growing on the banks. The wet creek margins are also an excellent place to search for turk's cap lily (Lilium superbum). These are spectacular plants growing more than seven feet high and producing numerous blossoms. The exotic-looking yellow-centered flowers have recurved orange petals that are speckled with black and have a prominent projecting stamen and anthers. In July, the lilies appear as small glowing embers within the shaded confines of the creek margins. Further away in the pines, there are populations of white-fringed orchid and nodding ladies tresses orchids (Spiranthes cernua) that bloom in late summer and early fall.

Complementing the surprisingly varied plant life in the preserve is an equally varied avian presence. Ponds that were created by damming the creek are used by migrating waterfowl, as well as resident ducks and geese. During summer large waders such as snowy egrets, great egrets, and great blue herons come to search for fish and frogs in the preserve's ponds. Many songbirds pass through during the migratory periods, and a healthy diversity of breeding songbirds still exists. Recently good numbers of red-bellied woodpeckers have established themselves here.

Opposite:
A red maple (Acer rubrum) in autumn color gracefully bends its branches over the still waters of the upper Connetquot River. Red maples and sour gums (Nyssa sylvatica) immediately flank the river, thriving in the wet boggy margin. Pitch pines (Pinus rigida) are visible behind them.

The Connetquot River
becomes progressively less
riverlike and more like a broad,
heavily vegetated swamp near
its headwaters.

Cinnamon ferns *(Osmunda cinnamomea)* in their golden autumn colors dominate the understory in these moist woodlands adjacent to the Connetquot River.

The common cattail *(Typha latifolia)* is an aquatic freshwater perennial that forms dense stands in shallow, still water. Both songbirds and water birds use the cover of cattail stands for nesting, and the plant's seed heads are a food source for birds, while muskrats favor the starchy roots.

Left:
Cattails and dew-covered grasses and marsh plants grow along the border of a stream at the Massapequa Preserve in Nassau County.

Page 156:
The Nissequogue River becomes a broad estuary subject to tidal fluctuations near the Long Island Sound. Vast areas of mud flats and tidal creeks appear twice a day.

Page 157:
Water parsnip *(Sium suave)* is one of many colorful wildflowers that bloom along the Nissequogue River.

Pages 158-59:
Broad-leaved arrowhead *(Sagittaria latifolia)* grow in the shallow water of a small pond created by damming a stream in Massapequa Preserve.

THE SOUTH FORK

The South Fork is the southernmost of the two great peninsulas that lie at Long Island's eastern end. It comprises the section of Long Island from Shinnecock Inlet to Montauk Point and represents a microcosm of almost all the natural habitats described in this book. The South Fork has a little bit of everything, from deciduous woodlands to maritime forests to pine barrens, as well as salt marshes, dune lands, rolling moors, the island's best sea bluffs, and even its own version of the Hempstead Plains. The shoreline of Montauk Point is a premonition of the rockbound New England coast.

Perhaps more than any other part of Long Island, the South Fork has been shaped by sea and wind. The forks are essentially piles of rubble arranged in long rows. As we have seen, during the last ice age the advances and retreats of several glaciers left high terminal piles of till, called moraines, in two long rows across the Long Island region. Water from melting glaciers raised the seas. The world's seas reached their present level about three thousand years ago, and in doing so filled the lowland between the two moraines in the east and giving rise to the forks. The Harbor Hill Moraine forms the North Fork while the Ronkonkoma Moraine creates the South Fork.

Four large bays—Great Peconic Bay, Little Peconic Bay, Gardiners Bay, and Napeague Bay—form the northern shoreline of the South Fork, creating the watery divide between it and the North Fork. Numerous sheltered harbors and marshes grace this ragged and deeply etched coast. One of the prettiest examples is Accabonac Harbor. Accabonac Harbor is a sheltered inlet with numerous coves and marshes, protected from Napeague Bay by two large sand spits that provide access to the harbor through one small channel. Along the sand spits are nesting common and least terns and also piping plovers. There are also several pairs of nesting osprey (Pandion haliaetus). Osprey, also called fish hawks, are just that, large raptors with a seventy-inch wingspan that feed almost exclusively on fish. Ospreys were once extremely abundant on Long Island. In the early nineteenth century, observers noted at least 300 nests on Gardiner's Island, and, in 1908, between 150 and 200 nests were counted, making it the largest osprey colony in the world. The density of breeders

was so great that, in 1958, at least sixty nests were found on the ground instead of in trees, an unusual accommodation to crowding by these arboreal nesters. By 1962, however, only twenty-one active nests were reported on Gardiner's Island.

It became apparent that DDT had caused the drastic reduction. DDT is a pesticide used for mosquito control. It is a highly stable and, therefore, long-lived chlorinated hydrocarbon that is passed up the food web, eventually becoming concentrated in predators at the top. In one study, DDT concentrations in Long Island Sound indicated a level of 0.000003 ppm (parts per million), while concentrations in local ospreys showed a level of 25 ppm, ten million times as much. DDT decomposes into DDE, which in birds inhibits the enzyme carbonic anhydrase, which in turn controls the calcium supply for shell formation. This caused the ospreys to lay thin-shelled eggs that are easily broken, thereby hampering their reproductive success. Not only osprey but other raptors, such as peregrine falcons (Falco peregrinus), were affected. During the 1970s, DDT was banned, and since then ospreys have made a substantial recovery.

The South Fork originally ended at Amagansett; the part of the Ronkonkoma Moraine from the present-day Hither Hills State Park to Montauk Point was an island, as Block Island, another remnant of the Ronkonkoma Moraine to the east of Montauk, is today. Over time, offshore currents deposited a series of sand spits on both the Amagansett and Montauk shores that eventually coalesced, bridging the four-mile gap between the two. Geologists give this type of formation the special name, "tombolo," but this sandy isthmus goes by the name given to it by

the Montauk Indians, Napeague, which is derived from the Indian words "niep," meaning water, and "eague," meaning land. It can be counted among the youngest lands in the country, being no more than three thousand years old and possibly quite less.

Today most of the Napeague dunes are within Napeague State Park, an interesting area where the ground, composed entirely of silica sands, supports a variety of vegetative covers. Not unexpectedly, pitch pines are abundant, given the dryness and sterility of the sand, but there are also pockets of water-loving shrubs, such as highbush blueberry. A large lens of fresh water exists just below the surface of the sand, formed by rainwater that percolates down through the sand until stopped by an impervious substrate below. In some places, the wind lifts sand from the ground and scrapes occur that are deep enough to intersect the water table. Over time, organic matter finds its way into these sandy pools, eventually forming a bog. Many small bogs of this type dot the Napeague dunes. Sphagnum moss dominates here as in the bogs of Long Island's central pine barrens. Cranberries are also particularly abundant in the bogs of the Napeague dunes. The curly grass fern (Schizaea pusilla), one of Long Island's rarest plants, grows in one bog in the Napeague dunes and nowhere else in New York State. This tiny fern, no more than two inches high, is completely unfernlike, with evergreen fronds that, as its name suggests, resemble curly grass more than anything else. One year I made several trips to seek this elusive fern. Curly grass fern easily becomes lost in the tangle of a bog, and it was not until my third attempt and after hours of careful searching that I found my prize.

The osprey *(Pandion haliaetus)*, or fish hawk, is once again a common breeding bird on Long Island. Ospreys have made a remarkable recovery after environmental pollution decimated their population during the 1960s and 1970s.

Opposite:
Seaweed, including green sea lettuce *(Ulva lactuca)*, green fleece *(Codium fragile)*, and rockweeds *(Fucus spp.)*, is exposed by the falling tide along the shore of Napeague Harbor.

Another rare plant growing here is the crested-fringed orchid *(Habenaria cristata);* this population represents the largest concentration in New York State.

The most unusual area around Napeague is the famous Walking Dunes, a complex of parabolic dunes that are just to the east of Napeague Harbor in Hither Hills State Park, a must-visit for anyone interested in Long Island's natural history. Parabolic dunes are U-shaped dunes that move, or "walk," under the influence of the prevailing winds. Napeague Harbor rests to the north of the Napeague isthmus and, like Accabonac Harbor, is protected from the open water by two large sand spits that project into Napeague Bay. The Walking Dunes formed on the eastern side of the bay.

The Walking Dunes are thought to be a relatively new addition to Long Island and probably caused by man. Maps of the area from 1845 show no evidence of the dunes and, in fact, indicate the area as being wooded with pitch pine. By 1892, maps show two distinct parabolic dunes and sand where the forest once stood. Possibly the disturbance in the area from fish factories built along the harbor during the 1860s and 1870s seeded the dune's formation. Activities such as road building, wood cutting, and the sinking of wells would have created open sandy areas where a blow out could occur. Blow outs are spots where vegetation has vanished from the dunes, causing the exposed sand to be lifted away by the wind. The shape and subsequent direction of the Walking Dunes support this hypothesis.

The largest dune moves as the prevailing winds off Napeague Harbor blow into the open end of the U facing the beach. The wind scrapes sand from the inside leading edge of the U and forces it forward and over the leading edge of the dune. As the Walking Dune moves, it covers trees in its path; many years later, a phantom forest of dead trunks appears as the dune moves on. At the top of the dune are buried trees, thirty feet tall, poking out of the sand.

Sand, then, is constantly being removed from the inside of the U, and if the scrape becomes deep enough groundwater will surface. This is what has happened in the hollow of the dune: it contains a cranberry bog. If you visit in June, the bog will be flushed with the bright pink blossoms of calopogon orchids *(Calopogon pulchellus)*, which are peculiar in that they have bearded upper petals, while most orchids in our area have bearded lower petals. The rose pogonia *(Pogonia ophioglossoides)* is another pink orchid that grows in this bog, although it is not as abundant as the calopogon. Another rare inhabitant is the thread-leaved sundew *(Drosera filiformis)*.

During wet summers, when standing water remains in the bog, a variety of amphibians breed there. Fowler's toads are common breeders, and, in good years, their tiny black tadpoles cover the bog's shallow bottom. A less common breeder is the eastern spadefoot toad *(Scaphiopus holbrooki)*, which, at one and a half to two and a half inches long, is smaller than Fowler's toad, with a dark back that often has two light, irregularly shaped lines. Small reddish tubercles cover its skin and its hind legs have a sickle-shaped projection used for digging. Spadefoot toads live a subterranean existence using the spade-like projections on their legs to shovel their way through the sandy soil. They wait for heavy

The tiny yellow flowers of
beach heather *(Hudsonia
tomentosa)* cover the
dunes in Napeague State
Park in June.

A cranberry bog lies within
the center of a large parabolic
dune at the Walking Dunes in
Hither Hills State Park. In early
June, the magenta blossoms of
calopogon orchids *(Calopogon
pulchellus)* rise above the
sphagnum and cranberries in
one of the island's most beautiful wildflower displays.

The rose pogonia
(*Pogonia ophioglos-soides*) is a delicately colored pink orchid that grows in the bogs of the Walking Dunes.

The eye of a spadefoot toad
(*Scaphiopus holbrooki*) carefully observes the environment as it emerges from its sandy burrow in the Walking Dunes. Spadefoot toads have small, spadelike projections on their hind legs that facilitate digging. They spend the entire year underground, coming to the surface to breed during periods of hard summer rains.

spring or summer rains and then emerge from their burrows to breed in the temporary rain pools that form. Their presence is made known by their loud and queer call that sounds like a dog barking. Eggs hatch within two days and complete metamorphosis from tadpole to adult takes two to eight weeks.

Beyond the forward edge of the dune is a small wetland with high-bush blueberry, royal ferns (*Osmunda regalis*), and swamp azalea (*Rhododendron viscosum*). Swamp azalea is a deciduous heath of wet soils that has a sweet-scented blossom in early summer. The species name *viscosum* means "sticky" in Latin, and the blossoms have a sticky goo on their long corollas. The pine woods beyond the wetland are dry, with no surface water present. In certain low areas between ancient dunes, there grows a species of orchid that appears to be unique. Until recently, most botanists thought it to be a form of the orange-crested orchid, but the color was very pale yellow and it grew in an uncharacteristically dry location. Observations and data have brought scientists to the conclusion that this is a new species of orchid, which has been named the pale-fringed orchid (*Platanthera pallida*). To date this is the only known location in the world for this plant.

The area of Napeague State Park south of Montauk Highway includes a wonderful stretch of Atlantic beach backed by a large primary dune. Behind this lie more dunes and swales interspersed among pitch pines. There are flats where beach grass and little blue stem grass predominate; in September, when the grasses have gone to seed, these places resemble nothing so much as a Kansas

prairie, dotted with blooming blazing star (*Liatris borealis*). Blazing star is another northern species whose small Long Island presence represents its southernmost range. These attractive rose-purple flowers on a flowering stalk two to three feet high are sometimes nipped in the bud by feeding deer.

One of the most outstanding features of the South Fork is the abundance and quality of its fresh-water wetlands. Swamps and numerous kettle ponds abound, but the crown jewel of the South Fork's wetlands must be the Long Pond Greenbelt. This consists of a narrow band of coastal plain ponds and wetlands extending southward about six miles from Sag Harbor to the Atlantic shore. More than thirty rare species live within this natural community, making it New York State's highest concentration of endangered species. Most of the rare organisms are wetland plants, including rose tickseed (*Coreopsis rosea*), drowned horn-rush (*Rhynchospora inundata*), and short-beaked rush (*Psilocarya nitens*). Tiger salamanders also use the ponds to breed, and this area remains the only place on Long Island where river otter (*Lutra canadensis*) live. The showpiece of this complex, and its largest body of water, is Long Pond where, in a marshy spot, there are several bald cypress trees (*Taxodium distichum*). Bald cypress are odd but compelling aquatic trees, being cone bearing but with deciduous needles. They grow with their roots submerged, and their trunks become swollen at the base. The recent discovery of these trees caused quite a bit of debate: bald cypress is a southern species whose northernmost population was previously known to be in Delaware. Although some debate continues, it appears that the bald cypresses in Long Pond are a natural population, representing an extreme northern limit for this species. Perhaps they are a relic from the height of interglacial warming some eight thousand years ago, when Carolinean zone vegetation extended further north.

To the south of Long Pond lies Poxabogue County Park, which, among other things, has nesting eastern bluebirds *(Sialia sialis)*. Their beauty and ubiquitous presence throughout New York resulted in the bluebird being named the state bird early in the century. Bluebirds, however, are cavity nesters that prefer open country. With the decline of farmland in New York and competition from nonnative cavity nesters, such as starlings *(Sturnus vulgaris)* and house sparrows *(Passer domesticus)*, bluebirds nearly vanished. Thanks to a widespread effort of nest box building by bird-watchers throughout the Northeast, bluebirds' numbers are increasing. The South Fork has several colonies, with the largest being in Cedar Point County Park.

South of Poxabogue Pond is a large primeval wetland, Sagg Swamp, the largest existing red maple swamp on the South Fork. The swamp is an eighty-four-acre wetland that is fairly intact, having not experienced any human disturbance since the late nineteenth century. Many of the red maples here have bearded lichen *(Usnea spp.)* growing on their branches. This attractive lichen, rare on Long Island, hangs from the trees like the crinkled beards of little old men. Sagg Swamp has an amazing diversity of plant life with more than 195 genera noted, including the easternmost occurrence of Atlantic white cedar on Long Island. It also seems to be the easternmost outpost for southern life of the Carolinean zone on

Long Island, indicated by the presence of southern flying squirrels *(Glaucomys volans)*.

The South Fork still has large tracts of undisturbed forest, with some of the best preserved woodlands located near Montauk. Together, Hither Hills State Park, the Hither Woods Preserve, and the Lee Koppleman Nature Preserve contain more than three thousand contiguous acres of woodlands. There is an interesting progression of forest type, as the Napeague pine woods of the west gradually transform into the Montauk heath system in the east. Most of the area consists of a transition forest of pine-oak mix, but there are also examples of oak-holly forest. Evidence of this region's glacial origins are evident everywhere. Most of the woodlands sit on top of the Ronkonkoma Moraine. Glacial erratics litter some spots, and there are long piles of boulders called boulder trains. To the north of the forest, there are high sand bluffs on Napeague Bay, a result of the endless wave action undercutting the high piles of glacial till.

Within the forest there are occasional high spots along the moraine devoid of the oaks and pines but brimming with grasses of various species. The best example is Ram Level, the largest and one of only five remaining maritime grasslands on Long Island (two, at Montauk Mountain and the high ground at Montauk County Park, are more easily accessible). At one time maritime grasslands covered hundreds of acres on Montauk. Their origin is unclear, but fire does play a role in their maintenance and past livestock grazing probably contributed as well. Ram Level is dominated by wavy hair grass, little blue stem, and Indian grass. In late summer

The yellow-fringed orchid *(Habenaria ciliaris)* is a very rare plant in New York State but several colonies exist on Long Island's South Fork. Despite their name, specimens on Long Island have an orangy color.

In the phantom forest, the stumps of pitch pines buried years ago reappear as the Walking Dune moves onward.

Left:
The buried tops of trees twenty-five to thirty feet high poke through the top of the Walking Dune.

The spring-fed Big Reed Pond
in Montauk County Park is one
of Long Island's most beautiful
and untouched bodies of water.

Opposite:
Montauk Mountain is a high
point of land that overlooks Fort
Pond to the west of Montauk
village. Its top harbors one of
the best examples of maritime
grasslands left on Long Island's
South Fork.

Oyster Pond in Montauk Point State Park has one of the northernmost populations of southern leopard frog. Here a breeding pair is seen in amplexis.

Box turtles (*Terrapene carolina*) are common inhabitants on Long Island's South Fork and are particularly abundant in the Montauk area. This wary turtle is peaking out from the protection of his tightly closed shell to see if danger has passed.

Opposite:
Little Sebonac Creek flows through the Scallop Pond Preserve near Cow Neck.

and early autumn, the brilliant blossoms of various goldenrods (*Solidago spp.*) and asters accent the golden browns of the grasses.

The Montauk moorlands are a different sort of high, open area, dominated by low heaths and other stunted shrubs. Many high spots of the Ronkonkoma Moraine that are close to the shore show this plant community. The poor sandy soils and the constant salt-spray pruning by the prevailing offshore winds both stunt and shape the growth. The moorlands grow on ground with a high water table; consequently there are many streams and boggy depressions. One of the few places on Long Island where the arethusa orchid (*Arethusa bulbosa*) grows is within these wetlands. Dragon's mouth is another name for this six- to ten-inch-high plant that produces a two-inch flower that looks like an open reptilian mouth with its tongue sticking out.

Box turtles (*Terrapene carolina*), terrestrial creatures that have a diverse diet ranging from worms and slugs to berries and mushrooms, are common here. They have a colorful carapace (top of the shell) with yellow, orange, and dark markings shaped something like a World War II army helmet. And, like a soldier's helmet, the shell of the box turtle offers it protection from enemies. The box turtle has a hinged plastron (underside of the shell) and is able to withdraw its head, tail, and limbs and close the plastron, forming a tightly sealed box. Undisturbed adult box turtles may live their entire life in an area as small as several acres. They have few enemies, and some individuals live more than one hundred years. Despite this, their numbers have been steadily declining due to loss of habitat, overcollecting, and

other pressures. Once widespread across the island, they now regularly occur only in undeveloped areas like the moorlands and pine barrens.

Another animal of the moors is the gray fox (*Urocyon cinereoargenteus*), but unlike the box turtle, it is extremely rare. Once common on Long Island, it is now known only to live in the Montauk area, although its present status remains in question. Both the gray and red foxes have variable color phases, and the best way to differentiate the two species is by the color at the tip of the tail. In all color phases, the gray fox has a black-tipped tail while the red fox has a white tip. The gray fox also differs from the red fox, as well as from all other native North American canids, in being able to climb trees.

In southern Montauk, on a state park that was once part of the U.S. Airforce's Camp Hero, there is a beautiful maritime American holly forest, second only to the hollies of Sunken Forest on Fire Island. Clear streams flow through this area, and there are many swampy depressions and small ponds. One of the most interesting creatures found here is the blue-spotted salamander (*Ambystoma laterale*). This member of the mole family of salamanders has the most northern distribution for that family. Like other mole salamanders, blue-spotted salamanders spend most of their time underground, making appearances on the surface only to breed. They have jet-black bodies decorated with small bluish and white metallic-looking specks.

Although blue-spotted salamanders are fairly common throughout their range, they only occur on Long Island in this area and are of special interest because of their genetic makeup. The last ice age forced blue-spotted salamanders

A seaside goldenrod (*Solidago sempervirens*) tenaciously grows from an eroded rut along the Montauk Bluffs. Seaside goldenrod is a succulent perennial wildflower with a deep root system, making it resistant to water loss and enabling it to thrive in dry sandy conditions. It blooms late in the season and is common to Long Island's coastal areas.

Opposite:
Wave action from the Atlantic Ocean is slowly eroding the bluffs formed by the Ronkonkoma Moraine at Montauk Point State Park.

to move south, creating populations such as the one on Long Island. Later, when the glaciers retreated, rising waters forced blue-spotted salamanders to move to the west. In doing so, they crossed paths with the similar Jefferson salamander *(Ambystoma jeffersonianum)* that was moving north. The two species interbred, creating strange genetic hybrid combinations with individuals containing the normal two (diploid) but also three (triploid) and four (tetraploid) sets of chromosomes. The result of this clash between the two species resulted in populations looking like Jeffersons, but containing blue-spotted genes and vice versa. The only populations of genetically pure blue-spotted salamanders known are from Prince Edward Island, Canada, and Montauk, Long Island. Being islands, these locations isolated the blue-spotted salamanders from invasion by Jefferson salamander genes. So the Montauk blue-spotteds remain a curious example of the power of glaciers to both alter a species or protect and isolate it.

Oyster Pond, within walking distance from Montauk Point on the North Shore, is a large brackish pond fed by numerous freshwater springs and streams. It is a good spot for spotted turtles *(Clemmys guttata)* and the surest place on Long Island to find southern leopard frogs *(Rana sphenocephala).*

Finally, there is Montauk Point itself, a rugged peninsula of sand, gravel, and clay embraced on three sides by the cool and turbulent waters of the Atlantic Ocean. The ceaseless conflict here between water and land has created what many believe is the most beautiful scenery on Long Island. Along the southern shoreline west

of Montauk Point Lighthouse, wave action nibbles away at the glacial till of the Ronkonkoma Moraine daily, resulting in steep-faced bluffs thirty feet or more high. Parts of the bluffs exhibit spectacular hoodoo formations. These are the result of the differential erosion of soft sands and resistant clays within the bluffs. The action of wind and water washes away the sand, leaving bizarre fluted pinnacles of hard clay. The scene is not unlike the hoodoo formations of South Dakota's Badlands National Park. Sunrise light on the cliffs boldly highlights the bluffs' bands of iron-laden clay in a warm orangy glow.

Scattered haphazardly within the moraine are erratics from various points to the north that were ripped from their bedrock and transported to Long Island by the great ice sheets. As wave action washes the sand and clay of the bluffs out to sea, these boulders drop to the beach and remain there, being too heavy for the littoral drift to move. In this way, a boulder-strewn shoreline has developed below the cliffs. The beach here is also steeper than other beaches on Long Island, promoting the erosion of sand and resulting in the creation of tide pools among the rocks at low tide. In recent years, a small, cobbled cove west of the point has been used by harbor seals *(Phoca vitulina)* as a low tide haulout in winter months. During one day in January 1996, I counted twenty-eight there.

The surf around the point seems incredibly rough in the summer and in winter it gets even worse, but amazingly it is during the coldest months that the waters become literally choked with seabirds. Waterfowl and seabird populations of the far

north use the Montauk waters as a warmer winter retreat. White-winged scoters *(Melanitta fusca),* surf scoters *(Melanitta perspicillata),* and black scoters *(Melanitta nigra)* by the thousand are common. Red-throated loons *(Gavia stellata)* and common loons *(Gavia immer),* dressed in their wintery silver gray instead of their more colorful summer plumage, fish the waters as well. Birders flock to Montauk Point during the winter in numbers almost as great as the birds, hoping to get a glimpse of rarities such as razorbills *(Alca torda),* common murres *(Uria aalge),* or dovekies *(Alle alle).* Occasionally western rarities show up: recent years have yielded western grebe *(Aechmophorus occidentalis)* and black-billed magpie *(Pica pica).*

Opposite:
Sunrise light highlights suspended pebbles and boulders along with deep nooks and crannies on a section of bluffs on the Atlantic shore. The oxidation of small iron particles suspended in clay is responsible for the reddish color of the bluffs here.

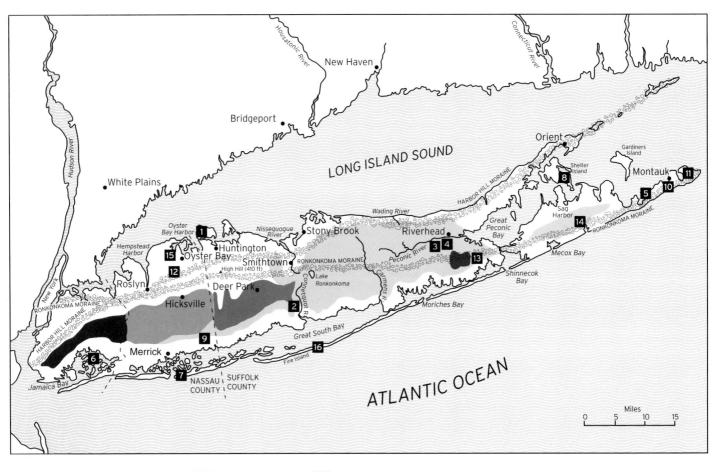

Housatonic River

Connecticut River

New Haven

Bridgeport

LONG ISLAND SOUND

HARBOR HILL MORAINE

Orient

Gardiners Island

White Plains

Hudson River

Shelter Island

Montauk

Wading River

Oyster Bay Harbor

Nissequogue River

Stony Brook

Riverhead

Great Peconic Bay

Sag Harbor

14

5

10

11

Hempstead Harbor

15

Huntington

Oyster Bay

Smithtown

1

8

RONKONKOMA MORAINE

Peconic River

3

4

13

RONKONKOMA MORAINE

High Hill (410 ft)

Lake Ronkonkoma

Carmens R.

Shinnecock Bay

Mecox Bay

12

NEW YORK

Roslyn

Deer Park

Connetquot R.

Moriches Bay

RONKONKOMA MORAINE

Hicksville

2

HARBOR HILL MORAINE

9

Merrick

Great South Bay

16

Fire Island

ATLANTIC OCEAN

6

7

Jamaica Bay

NASSAU COUNTY

SUFFOLK COUNTY

Miles

0   5   10   15

Brooklyn-Queens Barrens

Hempstead Plains

Oak Brush Plains

Pine Barrens

Dwarf Pine Barrens

Moraine

1. Caumsett State Park
2. Connetquot River State Park
3. Cranberry Bog County Park
4. David A. Sarnoff Preserve
5. Hither Hills State Park
6. Jamaica Bay Wildlife Refuge/
   Gateway National Recreation Area
7. Jones Beach State Park/West End
8. Mashomack Preserve/
   Shelter Island
9. Massapequa Preserve
10. Montauk Mountain
11. Montauk Point State Park
12. Muttontown Preserve
13. Quogue Wildlife Refuge
14. Sagg Swamp Preserve
15. Shu Swamp Preserve
16. Sunken Forest/
    Fire Island National Seashore

PLACES TO VISIT

Following is a list and description of some of the best places to see the natural wonders described in this book. Readers familiar with Long Island will discover omissions, but the list does not attempt to be a comprehensive inventory of the island's natural places. The listings below represent good examples of the major plant and animal communities on Long Island that are also easily accessible, and should serve only as a beginning for further explorations into nature on Long Island.

1. CAUMSETT STATE PARK

Caumsett State Park is located on Lloyd Neck in Suffolk County, and is owned and operated by the Long Island State Park and Recreation Commission. From Route 25A in Huntington turn north onto West Neck Road and travel approximately five miles. The park entrance is on the left. Park hours are from 8:30 A.M. to 4:30 P.M., and there is an entrance fee. For information call 516-423-1770.

Caumsett State Park offers open fields, upland woods, salt marshes, and one of the best-preserved cliffs on the Long Island Sound. It is a fifteen-hundred-acre preserve, originally part of the magnificent Marshall Field estate, whose buildings remain scattered across the grounds. There are trails and roads (including an extensive network of dirt roads that one can hike or bike along through upland woods) that provide easy access to most parts of the park.

The fields near the parking area, originally cleared in the 1920s for farming and maintained today by mowing, offer many possibilities for nature study. The most significant feature of Caumsett State Park, how-

ever, is the shoreline. There are wide-open views with few signs of development, and, on clear days, the shoreline of Connecticut is visible six miles across the sound. Thirty-foot-high bluffs of sand, gravel, and clay separate the beach from the woodlands. This is one of the few places on Long Island with exposed ancient Cretaceous Period sediments over sixty-five million years old. These are visible at the base of the cliffs, below younger sediments of glacial origin. The cliffs here exhibit hoodoo formations and, as at the Montauk Bluffs, bank swallows have nested in them.

If you walk along the beach to the west, you will come across a long gravel spit with a hook at its end, which creates a small harbor. The spit protects a large salt marsh with nesting ospreys. This is a good area for spotting red foxes, and I have seen them patrolling the edge of the marsh on more than one occasion. The marsh also has a population of sharp-tailed sparrows (*Ammodramus caudacutus*). These are secretive birds, rarely seen but commonly heard during the spring breeding season. They have a distinctive buzzy call, usually sung during the twilight hours.

2. CONNETQUOT RIVER STATE PARK

Connetquot River State Park is located in Oakdale, Suffolk County. The entrance is on the westbound side of Sunrise Highway. It is owned and operated by the Long Island State Park and Recreation Commission. You must obtain a permit to enter and there is an entrance fee of one dollar per person. The park is closed Mondays. For information write: Connetquot River State Park Preserve, P.O. Box 505, Oakdale, NY 11769; or call 516-581-2100.

Connetquot River State Park is a 3,473-acre sanctuary of undisturbed pine barrens, moist woods, and a pristine river, surrounded by suburban sprawl. There is a good system of trails, including a four-mile section of the Long Island Greenbelt trail, and numerous wood roads for exploration. An abundance and variety of wildlife and plants make this one of the finest parks for nature study on Long Island. There is also a nature center with informative displays and a red-marked trail through the wetlands along the river.

Connetquot's resident birds include some unusual species for Long Island. Several pairs of ospreys nest here, as do bluebirds in the open areas. It is, however, the occurrence of species that normally breed farther to the north that make the park so interesting. Extremely rare breeding birds for Long Island, including red crossbill (*Loxia curvirostra*), winter wren (*Troglodytes troglodytes*), and brown creeper (*Certhia americana*), breed here.

3. CRANBERRY BOG COUNTY PARK

Cranberry Bog County Park is located in Riverhead. From exit 71 off the Long Island Expressway take Route 24 (County Road 94) south to the Riverhead traffic circle. From the circle take Lake Avenue (County Route 63) 0.9 of a mile southwest to the preserve's gated entrance (there are no signs) on the right side of the road. You may park along the road without blocking the entrance. Access is by foot only.

Cranberry Bog County Park is an area of wild land whose habitats include pine barrens, an Atlantic white cedar swamp, and what is probably the island's largest bog. Parts of the park were run as a commercial cranberry bog beginning in the late nineteenth century. During that time, hundreds of acres of pine

barrens were cleared and sand was brought in to create a substrate for cranberry growth. The Little Peconic River was dammed, creating Sweezy Pond, which served as a reservoir for periodic flooding of the bog. Since termination of commercial operations, the farm's colonization by Long Island's bog-loving plants has brought the area back to a wild state. Today, Cranberry Bog stands as one of the best places on Long Island to observe Atlantic white cedar and bog communities.

A footpath winds its way around the perimeter of Sweezy Pond, crossing the Little Peconic River inlet to the pond at one point. From the eastern side of the pond, you look into a boggy area covered with sphagnum and small shrubs. Exploration of this area, although wet to the foot, will introduce you to a variety of bog vegetation. Two species of cranberry (*Vaccinium macrocarpon* and *Vaccinium oxycoccus*) wind their tiny vines through the sphagnum. The bog copper (*Epidemia epixanthe*), a rare butterfly of sphagnum bogs whose larva feed on cranberry, has a small colony here. Wetland plants like poison sumac (*Rhus vernix*) grow along the higher hummocks of land interspersed among the wet sphagnum. As expected, many carnivorous plants are present and thirteen species of orchids have been recorded in the bog.

The northern part of the park has one of the island's best remaining Atlantic white cedar groves. At the northern side of Sweezy Pond, a footpath branches to the north and leads to a wet area with many small white cedars. A larger cedar grove of more mature trees lies within the park around a pond to the north of Center Drive, several miles west of the Suffolk County Center. To the west of this pond, a small footpath leads in a northerly direction to the grove.

4. DAVID A. SARNOFF PRESERVE

The David A. Sarnoff Preserve is a state-owned 2,056-acre parcel of pine barrens near Riverhead. It can be reached by taking exit 71 off the Long Island Expressway and taking Route 24 to the Riverhead traffic circle. Turn right from the circle onto Lake Avenue (County Road 63) heading south and go 0.25 of a mile. The preserve entrance is on the left.

This is a good place to introduce yourself to the pine barrens without being consumed by its vastness. From the parking area it is possible to make a short loop that passes through the pine woods and by the shore of a beautiful pond, eventually returning to the parking lot. The woods are an excellent example of mature pine barrens, with large pitch pines (*Pinus rigida*) creating a canopy over a pinelands understory of bearberry (*Arctostaphylos uva-ursi*), bayberry (*Myrica pensylvanica*), huckleberries (*Gaylussacia spp.*), and more. In midsummer the pond is covered with the blossoms of the fragrant white water lily (*Nymphaea odorata*), and the pond's margins contain a number of interesting species of woody shrubs and flowering plants. In July look and smell for the blossoms of the clammy azalea (*Rhododendrom viscosum*) around the pond; their sticky, white flowers have a very strong sweet odor. The preserve is also a good area for locating a variety of bird species.

5. HITHER HILLS STATE PARK

Hither Hills State Park is located in the town of East Hampton, where Montauk Point State Parkway and Old Montauk Highway diverge eight miles west of Montauk Point. The park is owned and operated by the Long Island State Park and Recreation Commission. For information call 516-668-2461.

Hither Hills State Park is a diverse amalgam of 1,755 acres of woodlands, marshes, ponds, and dunes that has the Atlantic Ocean to the south and Napeague Bay to the north. The Atlantic shoreline has bathing beaches and a campground that makes an excellent, although buggy, spot to begin explorations of the area. The most interesting part of the park, however, is the Walking Dunes.

At the end of Napeague Harbor Road there is a trail leading to the Walking Dunes. It passes through a forest of stunted pitch pine, black oak (*Quercus velutina*), and scarlet oak (*Quercus coccinea*), punctuated by the dainty white blossoms of starflower (*Trientalis borealis*) growing in the shade of the trees. Starflower is a northern species at the southern limit of its range here on Long Island's coastal plain. This is an excellent spot from which to listen for the buzzing call of the prairie warbler, a common breeder here. The trail leaves the woods and encounters the steep western side of the largest parabolic dune. Continue by climbing to the top, where there are spectacular views in all directions. To the west is Napeague Harbor, to the south is the Napeague isthmus and the Atlantic, to the north Gardiners Island looms on the horizon, and to the east is the wild expanse of Hither Hills State Park. Looking to the east over the sand, you can see the line where sand and forest meet, marking the extent of the Walking Dune. You are standing on the western arm of the U-shaped dune and below you is the hollow forming the middle of the U. Continue down the hill and closer inspection will reveal the inside of the Walking Dune to contain a cranberry bog. Leaving the bog and heading toward the headwall of the dune, you will notice weathered trunks of trees emerging from the sand. This is the phantom forest. Continue up the headwall to the top, where before you are the tops of buried trees, thirty feet tall, poking out of the sand. Look over the side and see how the sands are encroaching on the forest ahead. Descending down the front of the dune, you will come to a small wetland.

From the parking lot where the trail to the Walking Dune begins you can also explore the shoreline of Napeague Harbor, walking all the way out to its mouth at the tip of Goff Point. The sand here is a beautiful orange color because it contains clay particles rich in iron. The origin of this material is a glacial stratum called the Plymouth Formation, found on terminal moraine along the shoreline to the west. The wrackline along the beach is usually littered with slipper shells and eel grass. The areas above the high-tide line have some unusual succulent beach plants, including seabeach sandwort (*Arenaria peploides*) and seabeach knotweed (*Polygonum glaucum*).

6. JAMAICA BAY WILDLIFE REFUGE/ GATEWAY NATIONAL RECREATION AREA

The Jamaica Bay Refuge is located in Broad Channel, Queens County, and is owned and operated by the National Park System. A parking area and visitors center is located on Cross Bay Boulevard, one and a half miles south of the North Channel Bridge in Howard Beach. The refuge is open daily from sunrise to sunset. For information call 718-318-4340.

Despite its location in one of the busiest urban centers in the world, the Jamaica Bay Wildlife Refuge is probably the best birding location on Long Island. There is no other single location on Long Island where you can see as many different species of birds in one day. To date the refuge has recorded 329 species of birds, from the tiny ruby-throated hummingbird to the huge golden eagle (*Aquila chrysaetosa*). The refuge, located within New York City limits and only two miles from John F. Kennedy International Airport, is an important stopover for the millions of migratory birds along the Atlantic flyway. It contains over 9,000 acres, but only about 250 acres are accessible on foot, the rest being small islands and marshes throughout Jamaica Bay.

From the visitors center, a 1.5-mile loop trail leads around a manmade freshwater pond called West Pond and then enters the north and south gardens before returning. The gardens consist of various species of trees and shrubs planted and maintained by refuge employees over the years to attract wildlife. Around the pond the trail is open, with views over the salt marsh. A spur trail off the main loop leads through the tern nesting area. This is a grassy spit of land that long ago had nesting terns. Terns no longer breed here, but the adjacent mud flats remain important feeding grounds for various shorebirds. The surrounding marshes are nesting areas for a number of species. My favorite is the boat-tailed grackle (*Quiscalus major*), a recent southern invader that got its footing on Long Island at Jamaica Bay. Boat-tailed grackles are big black birds that make weird noises that some people find annoying but I find delightful. Laughing gulls (*Larus atricilla*) are another new southern immigrant; within the last five years a huge colony of thousands has

established itself on the spartina marshes around the airport, which also contain the area's largest colony of marsh-nesting common terns. Common terns normally nest on sandy beaches, but here they lay their eggs on the mats of floating wrack that become entangled in the marsh. Despite their nests' precarious position at the edge of the water, the colony is growing. Yet another southern invader is the Forster's tern (*Sterna forsteri*). Several years ago a small colony appeared among the common terns. The only other colony on Long Island is in Hempstead Harbor.

The fall migration begins as early as July with southbound shorebirds, and continues through autumn, with songbirds and birds of prey, until there are thousands of waterfowl resting and feeding on the pond and surrounding bay. The manmade East Pond on the east side of Cross Bay Boulevard provides the greatest opportunity for observing migrating shorebirds. Each summer, refuge managers drop the water level on the pond, creating a vast area of mud flats that the shorebirds relish.

Jamaica Bay Wildlife Refuge holds other natural wonders besides its bird life. There is a great diversity of plant and insect life all around. The bay is rich with life as well. This becomes apparent during spectacles such as horseshoe crab egg laying in May or when the terrapin turtles leave the bay to lay their eggs in June. In some years, the autumn migration of monarch butterflies is as spectacular as the waterfowl's.

7. JONES BEACH STATE PARK/WEST END

Jones Beach State Park/West End is located in Wantagh, Nassau County, and is reached by traveling south on the Meadowbrook Parkway to its southern terminus, where you turn right onto Ocean Parkway. Follow Ocean Parkway for about one mile and turn right into the West End Boat Basin (directly next to the Coast Guard station) and park. From Memorial Day to Labor Day and on weekends from April 1 to Memorial Day and from Labor Day to Columbus day, a parking fee of four dollars per car is charged.

The immediate area of the boat basin is a superb place for birding. During both spring and fall migrations a variety of songbirds are present in the plantings around the area. On "wave days" thousands of northbound spring migrants fill the shrubs and ground, resting and feeding. The area consistently produces numbers of displaced birds from western and even European localities. I once documented an ash-throated flycatcher (*Myiarchus cinerascens*) there as well as western tanagers (*Piranga rubra*) on two occasions. These birds typically have a distribution well west of the Mississippi. The boat basin is very productive for birds in the winter as well. There are always common loons (*Gavia immer*) and red-throated loons (*Gavia stellata*) in the area as well as other wintering waterfowl. It is one of the surest places for observing wintering Bonaparte's gulls (*Larus philadelphia*). These birds nest to the north and west, primarily in interior areas, but winter on the East and West coasts. They are smaller than Long Island's familiar herring gull (*Larus argentatus*) and also differ in being highly acrobatic on the wing. They beat their wings rapidly and dive up and down in abrupt movements while fishing, appearing more like a tern than a gull.

From the boat basin you can walk west into the dunelands at the western end of the park. Colonial waterbirds such as common terns (*Sterna hirundo*) and black skimmers (*Rynchops niger*) have nested here but recently the colonies have fragmented and shifted. Shorebirds like the oystercatcher (*Haematopus bachmani*) and willet (*Catoptrophorus semipalmatus*) are common nesters and there are usually a few pairs of nesting piping plovers (*Charadrius melodus*) each year. Because of conservation efforts, the nesting areas of these birds are off-limits during the spring and summer. Some of the more interesting songbirds that nest in the area include the sharp-tailed sparrow (*Ammodramus caudacutus*) and the seaside sparrow (*Ammodramus maritimus*). A visit at dawn will let you hear the melodious callings of these birds that are usually hard to see. In winter the dunes are often visited by snowy owls (*Nyctea scandiaca*) and short-eared owls (*Asio flammeus*). These are species that nest in open tundra and prairie, respectively, and it is not hard to see

why they are attracted to the open dunes. Horned larks (*Eremophila alpestris*) and snow buntings (*Plectrophenax nivalis*) are two northern breeding songbirds of open country that are attracted to the dunes and beach during winter.

The west end dunes are also a wonderful place to observe the flora of Long Island's barrier beach dunelands. In spring the white blossoms of beach plum (*Prunus maritima*) border the dunes proper. Later in June the golden flowers of beach heather (*Hudsonia tomentosa*) carpet the dunes and in autumn the show of golden flowers continues with seaside goldenrods (*Solidago sempervirens*). In addition to plant life there exists some interesting fauna within the dunes. During wet springs certain depressions between dunes collect and hold water for several weeks. These interdune ponds become the homes of muskrats (*Ondatra zibethicus*) and the breeding pools for Fowler's toads (*Bufo woodhousei fowleri*).

Continuing through the dunes you will eventually reach the beach and the rocky jetty at Jones Inlet. In winter the rocks of the jetty are one of the surest places on Long Island to find purple sandpipers (*Calidris maritima*), named for the purple sheen to their winter plumage feathers visible when the light is just right. From the jetty you can return to the boat basin by walking east along the broad white sand beach that lies here and realize why Jones Beach is as attractive to humans as wildlife.

8. MASHOMACK PRESERVE/ SHELTER ISLAND

Shelter Island can be reached by taking the south ferry from Sag Harbor. From the south ferry port drive straight on Route 114 for 0.9 of a mile to the Mashomack Preserve, which is on the right. The preserve is open weekdays from May to September and weekends year-round. For information call 516-749-1001.

The Mashomack Preserve consists of 2,039 acres of an amazing diversity of natural habitats from pebbly shorelines and salt marshes to dense woodlands and open fields. There are about seventeen miles of trails that lead to most of the park's diverse ecosystems. Of special note is a unique pine swamp complex that is found nowhere else on Long

Island. The pine swamp has a lush growth of sphagnum moss so dense that there is little open water. White pines grow in the innermost parts of the swamp, whose perimeter is ringed by deciduous swamp species such as red maples, willows, and blueberries. The preserve's diversity of habitats attracts an even greater diversity of bird life, from tiny rubythroated hummingbirds to huge ospreys. At least eighty-two species of birds have been known to nest there. Equally interesting is the variety of plants found in the preserve, from rare species of orchids to the more familiar oaks and beeches, which grow in a 1,400-acre upland forest in the preserve. Mashomack is a wonderful place to spend the day and ranks among the island's finest places to observe nature.

9. MASSAPEQUA PRESERVE

Massapequa Preserve is located in Massapequa, and is owned by Nassau County. Its southern border is on Merrick Road and it continues north, crossing Sunrise Highway, until it reaches Southern State Parkway. It is most easily accessed from a small parking area on the northern side of Sunrise Highway, just east of the Massapequa train station. It can also be accessed just to the north of the parking areas along Clark Boulevard just west of its intersection with Lake Shore Road. For information call the Nassau County Parks Department: 516-785-2802.

Although it is a narrow piece of land surrounded by suburban housing sprawl, this preserve contains several wild areas with a surprising diversity of life. The preserve is easily accessed by a paved bicycle path that runs its length; there are also numerous footpaths through the wooded sections. The flora is different depending on whether you are north or south of Sunrise Highway, but through both sections there flows a small creek that has been dammed, forming several shallow ponds. North of the highway is a typical South Shore hardwood forest. The woodlands are primarily oak, with sweet gums and red maples in the moist margins of the wetlands.

South of Sunrise Highway, along with more deciduous woodlands there is also a small section of pine

barrens. A small prong of eastern Long Island's central pine barrens runs along the South Shore of Long Island through Nassau County, and the best remaining example of it is probably in this preserve.

10. MONTAUK MOUNTAIN

From Route 27 in Montauk follow Second House Road north 0.7 of a mile to an asphalt road on the left. Follow the road to the end and park. Walk up the dirt road on your left; the entrance to the preserve is at the end of the road past the last house on the right. The preserve is maintained by the South Fork Shelter Island chapter of the Nature Conservancy.

One of the best examples and most easily accessible of the maritime grasslands is at Montauk Mountain, a Nature Conservancy Preserve. Here there is a trail system that winds through oak and pine woods, where the rare bushy rockrose (*Crocanthemum canadense*) grows. On the height of land, the oaks give way to an open maritime grassland that is dominated by wavy hair grass and peppered with small shrubs. To the east there are excellent views over Fort Pond and the village of Montauk. Nantucket shadbush (*Amelanchier nantucketensis*), an extremely rare shrub, grows along the edges of the grassland.

11. MONTAUK POINT STATE PARK

Montauk Point State Park is administered by the Long Island State Park and Recreation Commission. It is located on the South Fork several miles beyond the village of Montauk at the end of Route 27. The park hours are sunrise to sunset and there is a parking fee. For information call 516-668-2461.

Montauk Point State Park includes more than 842 acres at the eastern tip of Long Island's South Fork. It is a rugged peninsula of sand, gravel, and clay embraced on three sides by the cool and turbulent waters of the Atlantic Ocean. The ceaseless conflict here between water and land has created what many believe is the most beautiful scenery on Long Island. The landscape along the southern shoreline west of Montauk Point Lighthouse is magnificent.

Here you will walk along a boulder-strewn beach beneath Long Island's most dramatic bluffs. Along parts of the bluffs you will find nesting burrows for bank swallows (*Riparia riparia*), which have become very rare on Long Island, and this colony is probably the surest place to see them. If you walk along the less rugged northern shoreline, you will eventually reach the inlet to Oyster Pond. During the winter months the northern shoreline usually yields the greatest numbers of wintering seabirds and seals.

12. MUTTONTOWN PRESERVE

Muttontown Preserve is located in East Norwich, Nassau County, and is owned and operated by the Nassau County Department of Recreation and Parks. The entrance is at the end of Muttontown Lane, south of Route 25A in East Norwich. The preserve headquarters and nature center are located next to a small parking lot at this entrance. Hours are 9:30 A.M. to 4:30 P.M. daily. Trail maps and seasonal guides are available. For information call 516-922-3123 or 516-922-2668.

A walk along the trails of Mutton-town Preserve will introduce you to some of the best examples of upland forests, morainal hills, and kettle ponds on Long Island. This preserve is a collection of various habitats, from moist woods to open fields, culled from the land of several former estates. The evidence of Long Island's glacial past is particularly strong among the five hundred or so acres that make up this preserve, highlighted by an excellent example of a glacial kame. A kame is a dome-shaped mound, formed when pebbles and sand accumulate in an opening in a motionless piece of glacial ice. Eventually the ice melts and the kame appears.

Just south of the kame is more evidence of glaciation in the form of several vernal kettle ponds. The woodlands here are lush with red maples and various oaks, and one kettle has a small grove of persimmon trees (*Diospyros virginiana*) on its shore. This is a rare plant on Long Island, since it is a southern species almost at the northern limit of its range. Persimmons have deeply furrowed bark with a pattern of small squares, making them easy to identi-

fy in summer; by autumn they are unmistakable with their fruit-laden branches. The round, orange fruit, about one and a half inches in diameter, remains on the tree well into winter when it becomes sweeter (immature fruit is high in tannin and therefore bitter tasting). The kettles here are also home to a number of amphibians, including breeding spadefoot toads, which are very rare in Nassau County, and there is a program to introduce tiger salamanders to the ponds. The surrounding woodlands abound with wildflowers typical of deciduous upland woods. The preserve boasts an impressive list of breeding woodland birds. A pair of great-horned owls take up residence here most years.

There are several open fields bordered by hedgerows that were farmed at one time. In late summer they are full of blooming goldenrod and asters and are particularly attractive to butterflies. The preserve is an outstanding place to find butterflies throughout the warm months, including many uncommon species for Long Island. A survey in July 1996 by the New York City Butterfly Club recorded a pipevine swallowtail (*Papilio philenor*) and a fiery skipper (*Hylephila phyleus*), two southern species rarely found on Long Island.

13. QUOGUE WILDLIFE REFUGE

Quogue Wildlife Refuge is located on Old Country Road, about half a mile north of its confluence with Montauk Highway in the town of Quogue, Suffolk County. The refuge is owned by the Southampton Township Wildfowl Association and managed by the New York State Department of Environmental Conservation. For information call 516-653-4771.

This is a small (two hundred acres) but extremely diverse preserve where it is possible to see a variety of Long Island's plant and animal communities. More than eight miles of footpaths wind through a variety of habitats, including tidal estuaries, pine barrens, dwarf pine barrens, freshwater ponds, bogs, and swamps. There is a visitors center with interpretive displays, as well as an animal pen and rehabilitation center where injured animals unable to return to the wild are kept. A large manmade

pond near the pens was built as part of an ice business that closed in the 1930s. The pond's drainage feeds south into Quantuck Creek, eventually draining into Quantuck Bay. It is an excellent place to observe migrating waterfowl, especially during the autumn flight. Breeding waterfowl include Canada geese (*Branta canadensis*), black ducks (*Anas rubripes*), mallards (*Anas platyrhynchos*), and wood ducks (*Aix sponsa*). In the summer the pond is one of the surest places on Long Island to find spotted turtles (*Clemmys guttata*).

A trail system leading north from the pens winds through a pine barren forest of pitch pine and scrub oak, with occasional scarlet and black oaks as well. The trail reaches the north end of the main pond, where a small boggy area exists, a good place for pitcher plants (*Sarracenia purpurea*) and sundews (*Drosera*). Farther to the north, the trail passes another pond before entering a section of the dwarf pine barrens. The transformation from normal pine barrens to pygmy pines is dramatic. Here the ground is dry and covered with bearberry and scrub oak, while the pygmy pines with their contorted and twisted branches stand as sentinels to a bizarre landscape.

This is an excellent area to observe the wildlife of the dwarf pines. Deer are plentiful, evidenced by their ubiquitous tracks along the sandy paths. During the summer the buzzing call of prairie warblers (*Dendroica discolor*) can be heard from all directions. Later in October, long after the prairie warblers have moved south, you may see buck moths (*Hemileuca maia*) on their courtship flight.

Finally there is access to Quantuck Creek by walking diagonally south from the refuge parking lot and crossing Old Country Road. Trails with observation areas look out over this pleasant estuary that is frequented by egrets, herons, and waterfowl.

14. SAGG SWAMP PRESERVE

The Sagg Swamp Preserve is located in Bridgehampton and is owned and operated by the South Fork Shelter Island chapter of the Nature Conservancy. Heading east on Route 27 from Southampton, turn right at the stoplight in Bridgehampton onto Ocean Road. Turn left on

Sagaponack Road and drive for 0.7 of a mile; a sign marking the preserve will be on the left just before the bridge over Sagaponack Pond.

At this preserve a trail leads you first through dry ground dominated by oaks and then through a red-maple swamp, bringing you close to the edge of an infamous sphagnum bog. The most interesting parts of the swamp lie off the trail in the bog, but the muck here is notorious. I once became stuck up to my knees. Don't worry, for the less adventurous there is enough well-constructed trail to make a visit worthwhile. The swamp probably formed as a series of connected kettle ponds gradually filled. Jeremy's Hole is the only remaining kettle with open water and lies more or less in the center of the preserve.

Within the swamp are the island's most easterly stands of Atlantic white cedar (*Chamaecyparis thyoides*) along with a long list of other rare and unusual plant species. Many of the trees and shrubs in the swamp appear to have what look like tufts of pale green garlands hanging from their branches. This is a species of lichen called old man's beard (*Usnea cavernosa*). This species likes moist environments and is also extremely sensitive to air quality and therefore is rare on Long Island. The only other place I know of where it regularly occurs is in Red Maple Swamp near Riverhead. Also of special note is the presence of southern wild raisin (*Viburnum nudum*). This is a handsome shrub with shiny, leathery leaves that grows fifteen to twenty feet tall. In June it has tiny white flowers in clusters that produce small dark edible fruits. The plant is most striking in autumn when the leaves take on a brilliant red color.

Many species of mammals call Sagg Swamp home including Long Island's most eastern population of southern flying squirrels (*Glaucomys volans*). On a winter visit to the swamp in 1994 I observed a mink (*Mustela vison*) feeding on the carcass of a black duck. Minks are members of the weasel family and are apparently present in good numbers throughout the South Fork of Long Island. They are close relatives to skunks and just like their stinky cousins possess anal glands that produce a fetid discharge, which minks primarily use to mark territory.

15. SHU SWAMP PRESERVE

Shu Swamp Preserve is located in Mill Neck, Nassau County. It is owned and operated by the North Shore Wildlife Sanctuary, Inc. Shu Swamp can be reached by turning north off Route 25A onto Wolver Hollow Road and following that until it becomes Chicken Valley Road and then Oyster Bay Road. From here turn right on Frost Mill Road and continue to the preserve entrance on the right immediately before the Mill Neck Railroad Station on the left. The preserve is closed on Fridays. For information call 516-671-0283.

Shu Swamp Preserve is an excellent example of the freshwater spring and stream complexes once very common on Long Island's North Shore. The preserve has marked hiking trails through woodlands and along streams, including a boardwalk trail over a freshwater swamp. The swamp's flora is amazingly diverse, as is the bird life. The least bittern (*Ixobrychus exilis*) and Virginia rail (*Rallus limicola*), although rare on Long Island, have bred in the swamp. Amphibians and reptiles are well represented with an especially strong population of snapping turtles (*Chelydra serpentina*). In June the snappers are often seen laying their eggs in the gravelly slopes along the Long Island Railroad tracks that border the preserve's north side.

The wet woodlands surrounding the swamp and streams are home to a magnificent stand of tulip trees (*Liriodendron tulipifera*), with some specimens reaching one hundred feet. Woodland birds abound and spectacular species such as the great-horned owl (*Bubo virginianus*) and wood duck (*Aix sponsa*) favor the primeval nature of the tulip grove, which is probably about 150 years old. There are good numbers of mammals including the familiar muskrats (*Ondatra zibethicus*) and chipmunks (*Tamias striatus*) and at least one not-so-familiar species. During one August in 1987 I discovered a female longtail weasel (*Mustela frenata*) and her young at the stump of a rotting tulip tree. Shu Swamp is a wonderfully compact preserve with an amazing variety of beauty and living things in any season, and a visit there will not disappoint you.

16. SUNKEN FOREST/FIRE ISLAND NATIONAL SEASHORE

The Sunken Forest is owned by the National Park Service and located on Fire Island in Sailor's Haven. It can be reached via ferry from May through November from Sayville, Suffolk County. Take Lakeland Avenue south from Sunrise Highway until reaching Main Street in Sayville and follow the green and white signs to the ferry. For the visitors center call 516-597-6183 and for ferry information call 516-589-8980.

The Sunken Forest is Long Island's finest example of a barrier island maritime forest. At the ferry dock there is a visitors center. A boardwalk enters the forest through a grove of shrubby Juneberry trees (*Amelanchier canadensis*) with branches that have been twisted in the wind like corkscrews. Unexpectedly, the trail winds through several small swampy areas where fresh groundwater reaches the surface and sphagnum moss, red maple (*Acer rubrum*), and highbush blueberries (*Vaccinium corymbosum*) thrive. You will soon enter an area that contains Long Island's largest stand of American holly (*Ilex opaca*). Along the way, watch for deer that like to rest in the shade of the hollies during the heat of a summer's day.

The boardwalk makes a small loop through a marshy open area, leading to the north shore of Fire Island on the Great South Bay. Strong wave erosion has made the beach here very narrow. The boardwalk continues through the forest, finally climbing over the secondary dune and into the interdune swale. Instantly the ecology changes from a shaded moist forest to a dry desertlike environment dominated by heather, bearberry, and beach grass. From here you can cross over the primary dune to the Atlantic shoreline.

BIBLIOGRAPHY

Albright, Rodney, and Priscilla Albright. *Short Nature Walks on Long Island*. 3rd ed. Chester, Conn.: Globe Pequot Press, 1988.

Art, Henry Warren. *Ecological Studies of the Sunken Forest Fire Island National Seashore New York*. Washington, D.C.: National Park Service Scientific Monograph Series No. 7, 1976.

Blumer, Karen. *Long Island Native Plants for Landscaping: A Source Book*. Brookhaven, N.Y.: Growing Wild Publications, 1990.

Bookbinder, Bernie. *Long Island: People and Places, Past and Present*. New York: Harry N. Abrams, 1983.

Bull, John. *Birds of the New York Area*. New York: Dover, 1964.

Campbell, Neil A. *Biology*. 3rd ed. Redwood City, Calif.: Benjamin-Cummings, 1993.

Cobb, Bougnton. *A Field Guide to the Ferns*. Boston: Houghton Mifflin Co., 1963.

Conant, Roger. *A Field Guide to Reptiles and Amphibians of Eastern/Central North America*. Boston: Houghton Mifflin Co., 1975.

Field Guide to the Birds of North America. Washington, D.C.: National Geographic Society, 1983.

Fuller, Myron L. *The Geology of Long Island, NY*. United States Geological Survey Paper No. 82231p., 1914.

Gabriel, Ralph Henry. *The Evolution of Long Island: A Story of Land and Sea*. New Haven: Yale University Press, 1960.

Griffith, William T. *South Fork Shelter Island Preserve Guide*. Sag Harbor, N.Y.: The Nature Conservancy, 1990.

Hoyt, Erich. *The Whale Watcher's Handbook*. Toronto, Canada: Penguin Books, 1984.

Johnson, Ann F. *A Guide to the Plant Communities of the Napeague Dunes Long Island, New York*. Southampton, N.Y.: Ann F. Johnson, 1985.

Johnson, Madeleine C. *Fire Island*. Mountainside, N.J.: Shoreland Press, 1983.

Kulik, Stephen. *The Audubon Society Field Guide to the Natural Places of the Northeast Coast*. New York: Pantheon Books, 1984.

Long, Robert P., William Wilheim, and Barbara Wilheim. *Canoeing the Carmens River*. Cutchogue, N.Y.: Peconic Publishers, 1985.

Long, Robert P., William Wilheim, and Barbara Wilheim. *Canoeing the Peconic River*. Cutchogue, N.Y.: Peconic Publishers, 1983.

Mannello, George. *Our Long Island*. Malabar, Fla.: Robert E. Krieger Publishing Co., 1981.

Murphy, Robert Cushman. *Fish-shaped Paumanok*. Great Falls, Va.: Waterline Books, 1964.

Niering, William A. *The Audubon Society Field Guide to North American Wildflowers: Eastern Region*. New York: Alfred A. Knopf, 1979.

Niering, William A. *Audubon Society Nature Guides: Wetlands*. New York: Alfred A. Knopf, 1985.

Paul, Lawrence G. *The Pine Barrens of Ronkonkoma*. New York: New York-New Jersey Trail Conference, 1986.

Peterson, Roger Tory, and Margaret McKenny. *A Field Guide to Wildflowers: Northeastern/Northcentral North America*. Boston: Houghton Mifflin Co., 1968.

Puleston, Dennis. *A Nature Journal*. New York: W. W. Norton & Co., 1992.

Richard, Glenn A. *A Beachcomber's Guide to Long Island's Shores*. Stony Brook, N.Y.: Museum of Long Island Natural Sciences, 1979.

Richard, Glenn A. *The Long Island Pine Barrens: Our Fragile Wilderness*. Stony Brook, N.Y.: Museum of Long Island Natural Sciences, 1979.

Richard, Glenn A. *Tall Grass by the Sea: A Guide to Long Island's Salt Marshes*. Stony Brook, N.Y.: Museum of Long Island Natural Sciences, 1979.

Robins, C. Richard, Ray G. Carleton, and John Douglass. *A Field Guide to Atlantic Coast Fishes of North America*. Boston: Houghton Mifflin Co., 1986.

Schubel, J. R. *The Great South Bay*. Stony Brook, N.Y.: Marine Science Research Center, n.d.

The Sound Book. Norwalk, Conn.: Long Island Soundkeeper Fund Inc., 1992.

Stalter, Richard. *Barrier Island Botany*. Dubuque, Iowa: Wm. C. Brown Publishers, 1992.

Sutton, Ann, and Myron Sutton. *Audubon Society Nature Guides: Eastern Forests*. New York: Alfred A. Knopf, 1985.

Turner, John L. *Exploring the Other Island: A Seasonal Guide to Nature on Long Island*. Great Falls, Va.: Waterline Books, 1994.

Whitaker, John O., Jr. *The Audubon Society Field Guide to North American Mammals*. New York: Alfred A. Knopf, 1980.

Yeaton, Sam. *A Natural History of Long Island*. Cold Spring Harbor, N.Y.: The Nature Conservancy, 1973.

ACKNOWLEDGMENTS

Over the years I have had the good fortune to meet a great many people who, like me, have a great love for Long Island's natural wonders. I extend my thanks to all those individuals I encountered while working on this book who so openly shared their knowledge of Long Island with me. I would especially like to thank the following people for their help in creating this book: Don Riepe of the American Littoral Society, Mike Bottini of the Group for the South Fork, Otto Heck of the Long Island Nature Conservancy, Maxwell Cohen, Jeff Ritter, Arthur Berland, Dave Taft, John Smith, Sherman Wolfson, Carl Howard, Judi Zygelman and Uncle Nard, and my father, Maurice Villani, for turning me on to really neat rocks at Montauk sometime in the late '60s. At Abrams, I would like to thank Sheila Franklin for first showing interest in this book, now almost ten years ago, and making the project a reality. Ellen Nygaard Ford for her beautiful book design. And finally, my editor, Eric Himmel, for his expertise and hard work. His input elegantly tied together all my loose ends.

ABOUT THE PHOTOGRAPHS

The landscape photographs and many of the close-ups were taken with a Toyo 45A 4x5 field camera. I used 210mm and 90mm Schneider lenses. A variety of 4x5 films were used, including Fuji RDP-100 and provia, Ektachrome 100, and Polaroid prochrome. Most of the exposures were calculated with a Gossen LunaPro light meter. An 81A warming filter and a split neutral density filter were used occasionally. The wildlife photographs and most of the close-ups were taken with a Canon F1 35mm camera. I used the Canon 500mm, 80-200mm, 200mm macro, and 20-35mm L series lenses. All of the 35mm photographs were taken with Kodachrome 64 film except for a few where I used Fujichrome 100. I used a Gitzo 210 tripod with an Arca Swiss ball head. My backpack of photo equipment was typically over 50 pounds.

INDEX

Note: Page numbers in italics refer to illustrations.